WHAT DO YOU CALL
A SOCIOPATH
IN A CUBICLE?

(ANSWER:
A COWORKER)

Other DILBERT books from Boxtree

Another Day in Cubicle Paradise
ISBN: 0-7522-2486-7

When Did Ignorance Become a Point of View
ISBN: 0-7522-2412-3

Excuse Me While I Wag
ISBN: 0-7522-2399-2

Dilbert-A Treasury of Sunday Strips: Version 00
ISBN: 0-7522-7232-2

Random Acts of Management
ISBN: 0-7522-7174-1

Dilbert Gives You the Business
ISBN: 0-7522-2394-1

Don't Step in the Leadership
ISBN: 0-7522-2389-5

Journey to Cubeville
ISBN: 0-7522-2384-4

I'm Not Anti-Business, I'm Anti-Idiot
ISBN: 0-7522-2379-8

Seven Years of Highly Defective People
ISBN: 0-7522-2407-7

Casual Day Has Gone Too Far
ISBN: 0-7522-1119-6

Fugitive from the Cubicle Police
ISBN: 0-7522-2431-X

Still Pumped from Using the Mouse
ISBN: 0-7522-2265-1

It's Obvious You Won't Survive by Your Wits Alone
ISBN: 0-7522-0201-4

Bring Me the Head of Willy the Mailboy!
ISBN: 0-7522-0136-0

Shave the Whales
ISBN: 0-7522-0849-7

Always Postpone Meetings with Time-Wasting Morons
ISBN: 0-7522-0854-3

WE'VE NEGOTIATED THIS CONTRACT FOR SIX WEEKS AND TODAY YOU DOUBLE YOUR DELIVERY TIME?

I CAN'T TELL IF YOU'RE AN INCREDIBLY DEVIOUS WEASEL OR SIMPLY INCOMPETENT.

HERE'S A CLUE.

POINK

HEY, WE NEGOTIATED THIS DEAL IN ENGLISH BUT YOUR CONTRACT IS INCOMPREHENSIBLE WEASELEZE!

MY ONLY CHOICES ARE TO SIGN SOMETHING I DON'T UNDERSTAND OR GET MY LAWYER INVOLVED AND MISS MY DEADLINE!

HA! NOW YOU'RE GOING TO HECK!

ARE YOU HASSLING MY FRAT BROTHER?

CARL, YOU'RE ONLY A CONTRACTOR. YOU HAVE TO STOP USING COMPANY RESOURCES.

MMN NPH HBM MRM!

YES, I KNOW YOU BRING YOUR OWN AIR, BUT YOU STILL USE OUR GRAVITY.

FBM GMP RKR!

IF IT'S NOT TOO MUCH TO ASK, COULD YOU HOVER?

ANNE L. RETENTIVE

ANNE, I'M GOING TO TASK YOU WITH A DELIVERABLE.

GAAA!! TASK IS NOT A VERB!! MY WORLD IS FALLING APART!

TOMORROW I'LL ASK HER TO TIMELINE HER PROJECT.

I HAVE DISCOVERED THE CAUSE OF OUR NETWORK OUTAGES.

LAN

SOME IDIOT IS USING OUR NETWORK ROOM FOR MEETINGS AND UNPLUGGING THE SERVER BECAUSE IT'S TOO NOISY.

A SERVER IS LIKE A WAITRESS, RIGHT?

YEAH, A NOISY ONE.

ASK THE TROLLS IN ACCOUNTING TO EXPLAIN THIS CHARGE.

GAA!

PLEASE DON'T MAKE ME TALK TO THE TROLLS DURING BUDGET SEASON!

NEXT

ACCOUNTING TROLLS

I NEED AN EXPLANATION FOR THESE NUMBERS.

THIS IS BUDGET SEASON SO I WILL SPIT ON YOUR DATA AND SEND YOU AWAY.

THAT DOESN'T SOUND TOO BAD.

OUR BODIES ARE 95% MADE OF SPIT.

ACCOUNTING TROLLS

GO AHEAD, LARRY SPIT ON HIS DATA.

PTOO!!

CAN I GIVE YOU A LITTLE TOUR OF OUR DEPARTMENT?

TOUR OF ACCOUNTING

OVER HERE WE HAVE OUR RANDOM NUMBER GENERATOR.

NINE NINE NINE NINE NINE NINE

ARE YOU SURE THAT'S RANDOM?

THAT'S THE PROBLEM WITH RAN- DOMNESS: YOU CAN NEVER BE SURE.

WERE YOU ALWAYS A TROLL?

NO, THIS HAPPENED WHEN I CAME TO ACCOUNTING.

FIRST MY HAIR FELL OUT. THEN I STOPPED GOING TO THE GYM.

YOU HAVE HORNS AND A TAIL.

WHEN I REALIZED I HAD A LOOK GOING I JUST WENT FOR IT.

SO, IF ALL TROLLS WERE ONCE PEOPLE, THAT MEANS SOME PEOPLE ARE ALREADY CHANGING AND DON'T KNOW IT.

EXACTLY

THIS IS THE LIST OF PEOPLE WE'RE WAITING FOR.

♫ I KNOW ♫ SOMETHING YOU DON'T KNOW ♫

I THINK I'M GETTING PIMPLES ON MY HEAD.

Since its debut in 1989, *Dilbert* has kept the working world in stitches, attracting fans from all cubicles and corridors of white-collar existence. This sixth *Dilbert* treasury, *What Do You Call a Sociopath in a Cubicle? Answer: A Coworker*, brings together all of the office psychos who have annoyed Dilbert and entertained millions over the past thirteen years. This compilation pays homage to some of the most annoying and outrageous characters Adams has ever drawn—characters he likes to call office "sociopaths."

This full-color treasury reinforces everything that makes the strip great by lampooning the people and processes of business. Adams homes in on all the quirky coworkers and office oafs who drive us crazy in the corporate world—creatures like the Office Sociopath, who listens to voice mail on his speaker phone, and the Exactly Man, who punctuates everything with a finger point and a loud "Exactly!" The result is a book that leaves readers knowingly rolling their eyes and, of course, laughing uproariously.

Dilbert and his cube crew now appear in two thousand daily newspapers and are seen by 150 million people in sixty-five countries. They can be found on the Internet at www.dilbert.com.

BOXTREE

www.panmacmillan.com
www.dilbert.com
©2002 United Feature Syndicate, Inc.

WHAT DO YOU CALL A SOCIOPATH IN A CUBICLE?

(ANSWER: A COWORKER)

A DILBERT BOOK
BY SCOTT ADAMS

BOXTREE

First published 2002 by Andrews McMeel Publishing, 4520 Main Street, Kansas City, Missouri 64111, USA

This edition published 2002 by Boxtree
an imprint of Pan Macmillan Ltd
Pan Macmillan, 20 New Wharf Road, London N1 9RR
Basingstoke and Oxford
Associated companies throughout the world
www.panmacmillan.com

ISBN 0 7522 2417 4

9 8 7 6 5 4 3 2 1

A CIP catalogue record for this book is available from
the British Library.

Printed by The Bath Press Ltd, Bath

Yes, Pam, it's for you.

Introduction

I'm often asked if I think there are more sociopaths, morons, and lunatics in the workplace than anywhere else. It's a fair question, because it seems as if cubicles attract more than their fair share. But I have a different theory. I believe that everyone is a sociopath waiting to be discovered. Normally you can control your evil impulses. In fact, outside of work, you have to control yourself or you'll be beaten, disinherited, or jailed.

But at work, chances are you're already experiencing life at its worst. It's important to inject some entertainment into your day. And if that means making life miserable for your coworkers, many people seem willing to yank that thread. The only danger in being a workplace sociopath is that you can't be evil to your boss, your boss's secretary, customers, or anyone who is having an affair with your boss, because it'll come back to bite you. But anyone else is fair game, especially vendors and coworkers. Even if they complain, no one will listen. There's no downside to being a sociopath if you pick your targets carefully, and the entertainment value can be considerable.

Traditionally, every workgroup has at least one flaming @$$hole, one interminable bore, and one person who needs a metronome to remember to breathe. But thanks to technology, many new breeds of sociopaths have evolved. Far and away the most popular type is the guy who uses his speakerphone in the cubicle. I hear more complaints about that than about any other workplace issue. To the uninformed observer it might seem as though the speakerphone sociopath is oblivious to the anguish he causes to nearby cubicle dwellers. My theory is that he knows, and he enjoys making the people around him suffer. This is the same guy who raises new, unsolvable issues at the end of three-hour meetings. On some level, he thinks it's funny. There's no other way to explain it.

Speaking of abusing other people for entertainment, there's still time to join Dogbert's New Ruling Class (DNRC) and be by his side when he conquers the world and makes everyone else our domestic servants. To join, all you need to do is sign up for the free *Dilbert Newsletter* that's published approximately whenever I feel like it — about five times a year.

To subscribe or unsubscribe, go to www.dilbert.com. If you have problems with the automated subscription method, write to newsletter@unitedmedia.com.

S.Adams

Scott Adams

15

16

IT IS THE MOST
FEARED AND HATED
CREATURE ON EARTH

NOT A DINOSAUR

GRRRR

NOT A RABID DOG

RABID?

NOT DONALD TRUMP

IT IS THE "UGLY SINGLE MALE"

OTHER MALES FEAR BEING
ASSOCIATED WITH HIM

HI, GUYS!

WOMEN AVOID EYE CONTACT
AND FLEE IN HORROR

ANYBODY
FREE FOR
LUNCH?

ONLY A MAIDEN SACRIFICE
CAN END THE HORROR

WE DREW STRAWS;
I HAVE TO MARRY
YOU.

18

ASK MY SECRETARY TO SCHEDULE A MEETING.

GROAN

UH...EXCUSE ME ... EXCUSE ME ... MISS CERBERUS, COULD A HUMBLE EMPLOYEE HAVE THE HONOR OF YOUR ATTENTION?

ARE YOU PREPARED TO TAKE THE CHALLENGE OF DEATH ?!!

DOES THIS INVOLVE ANY WINGED MONKEYS ?

4-29

THE BOSS'S SECRETARY

YOU MUST PASS THE CHALLENGE OF DEATH BEFORE I PUT YOU ON THE BOSS'S CALENDAR.

BRING ME THE HEAD OF WILLY THE MAIL BOY !!!

GASP

HEY, WILLY, WOULD YOU LIKE TO SEE A TRICK ?

4-30

... SO, THEN MY BOSS'S SECRETARY, MISS CERBERUS, SAYS SHE WON'T PUT ME ON THE CALENDAR UNLESS I BRING HER THE HEAD OF WILLY THE MAIL BOY.

5-1

WHAT CHOICE DID I HAVE ?

I WENT BOWLING.

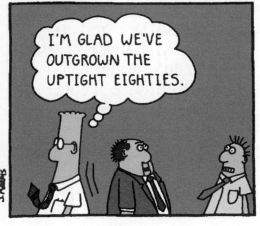

I'VE HIRED A CONSULTANT TO CLARIFY OUR COMPANY POLICY ON DISCRIMINATION.

IT IS AGAINST POLICY TO DISCRIMINATE BASED ON RACE, SEX, AGE, HANDICAP OR RELIGION

CONSULTANT

DOES THAT INCLUDE UNPOPULAR, LITTLE RELIGIONS?

NO, THOSE ARE CONSIDERED CULTS; YOU MAY DISCRIMINATE FREELY AGAINST THEM.

WHAT ABOUT SHORT, BALD, FAT, UGLY MEN? ARE THEY CONSIDERED "HANDICAPPED"?

TECHNICALLY, NO. YOU CAN STILL TEASE THEM AND DENY THEM PROMOTIONS AS USUAL.

© 1991 United Feature Syndicate, Inc.

S.Adams

LIKEWISE, YOU MAY DISCRIMINATE AGAINST NERDS, SMOKERS, AND SINGLE PEOPLE.

6-30

AND WE'VE DROPPED "STUPID PEOPLE" FROM THE WATCH LIST, AS THEIR LOBBYING EFFORTS PROVED INEFFECTIVE...

I THOUGHT IT WAS BAD WHEN THEY MADE US WORK IN THOSE LITTLE CUBICLES...

THEN THEY PUT TWO PEOPLE IN EACH CUBICLE... BUT WE GOT USED TO IT.

6-17

I GUESS WE'LL GET USED TO VELCRO STRIPS, TOO.

© 1991 United Feature Syndicate, Inc.

YEAH... I HAD A TEMPERATURE OF 147° AND THEY HAD TO REMOVE MY INTERNAL ORGANS.

WELL, THAT'S NOTHING COMPARED TO MY BOUT WITH BUBONIC PLAGUE LAST WEEK.

8-9

DID I EVER TELL YOU ABOUT THE TIME I REPAIRED MY OWN LAWN MOWER?

NOT AGAIN.

© 1991 United Feature Syndicate, Inc.

I DISAGREE WITH EVERYTHING YOU SAID. WHO WANTS TO STEP OUTSIDE AND FIGHT ABOUT IT?!!

I MAY BE ON THE SMALLISH SIDE BUT I CAN KICK ANY BUTT IN THIS ROOM!!

8-28

C'MON, WHO WANTS A PIECE OF ME??!

IT'S MY FAULT. I ACCIDENTALLY USED HIM TO SOAK UP A COFFEE SPILL THIS MORNING.

© 1991 United Feature Syndicate, Inc.

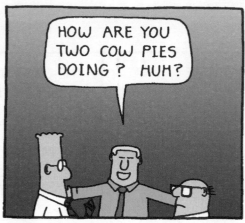

UH... WALLY, YOU'RE WEARING ONLY UNDERWEAR AT WORK.

I'M TRYING TO GET FIRED.

THE COMPANY LAYOFF PLAN IS VERY GENEROUS. I'LL GET A BIG PILE OF MONEY IF THEY ASK ME TO LEAVE.

THIS HAS GIVEN ME A DEGREE OF FREEDOM IN DEALING WITH LOCAL MANAGEMENT.

TED, CAN YOU EXPLAIN ITEM NUMBER TWO?

NO. I'M ON VACATION.

I TAKE MY VACATIONS IN TEN MINUTE INCREMENTS DURING REGULAR WORK DAYS. THAT WAY I CAN AVOID ASSIGNMENTS.

YOUR TEN MINUTES ARE UP.

COUGH COUGH! WHOA, I'D BETTER TAKE SOME SICK TIME.

DILBERT, YOUR NEW CO-WORKER IS ZIMBU THE MONKEY.

ZIMBU LEARNED ENGLISH FROM THE ZOO KEEPERS IN A SPECIAL PROGRAM.

THIS MONKEY IS AN INSULT TO THE INTELLIGENCE OF THE OTHER WORKERS AND I!

OTHER WORKERS AND "ME," NOT "I."

I'VE DECIDED TO HAVE PLASTIC SURGERY.

FRANKLY, I THINK IT'S THE RIGHT DECISION.

MAYBE THEN NOBODY WILL CALL YOU "TOUCAN SAM" BEHIND YOUR BACK IN THE CAFETERIA EVERY DAY.

OOH, AND REMEMBER WHEN THE SUMMER INTERN LEFT?

THE JOKE WAS "MAYBE JANET ACCIDENTALLY SNORTED HIM UP HER NOSE."

ACTUALLY, I'M ONLY GOING TO HAVE MY LIPS PUFFED.

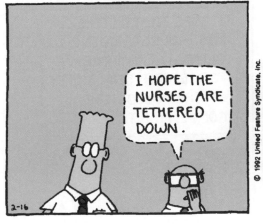

I HOPE THE NURSES ARE TETHERED DOWN.

I GOT OFF EASY... POOR NORMAN GOT SNORTED.

33

UH-OH... NEW FATHER COMING THIS WAY.

I'M OUT OF HERE.

HI, DILBERT. HAVE YOU SEEN MY BABY PICTURES YET?

GROAN

I'LL HAVE TO COME UP WITH TONS OF COMPLIMENTS OR I'LL SEEM SHALLOW.

THIS IS THE MOST BEAUTIFUL BABY IN THE UNIVERSE. LOOKS JUST LIKE YOU. SHE SHOULD BE A MODEL.

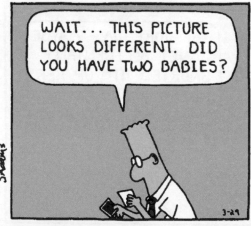

WAIT... THIS PICTURE LOOKS DIFFERENT. DID YOU HAVE TWO BABIES?

THE FIRST PICTURE WAS OUR PUG DOG, WINSTON. IT GOT IN THERE BY MISTAKE.

I HOPE THAT LITTLE MISUNDERSTANDING WON'T DETRACT FROM THE PERCEIVED SINCERITY OF THE FOLLOWING COMPLIMENTS...

© 1992 United Feature Syndicate, Inc.

34

HEY, THAT'S A GOOD TECHNIQUE: COMBING YOUR EAR HAIR OVER THE BALD SPOT!

I'VE BEEN WORKING ON THE EYEBROWS—COMBED-OVER-THE-HEAD METHOD.

SOMEBODY SHOULD TALK TO THAT MAN.

I'M FEELING CONFIDENT TODAY WITH WHAT APPEARS TO BE A FULL HEAD OF HAIR.

NOBODY SUSPECTS THAT I'M ACTUALLY COMBING THE HAIR THAT GROWS IN MY EARS OVER THE TOP OF MY OTHERWISE BALD HEAD.

IT'S AMAZING HOW CLUELESS THESE PEOPLE ARE.

MAYBE TED CAN ANSWER THAT QUESTION...

UH-OH

THEY'RE TRYING TO MAKE ME WORK. I'LL HAVE TO USE BODY LANGUAGE TO DISCOURAGE THEM.

UH... NEVER MIND

IT'S WORKING.

EVERYBODY IN THE OFFICE GETS A TURN HOLDING MY NEW BABY.

NEXT.

UH-OH... SNEEZE COMING.

ACHOOO

OOH! LOOK WHAT HE DOES WHEN YOU SNEEZE ON HIM.

HE LOOKS LIKE A PRUNE!

7-4

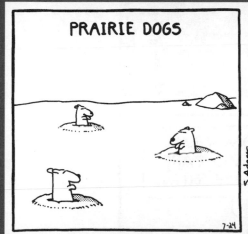

PRAIRIE DOGS

7-24

OFFICE WORKERS

PRAIRIE DOG WORKERS

MAN, I'M SWAMPED.

GEE, TIM, YOU LOOK AWFUL.

I'VE BEEN WORKING FOR FIVE DAYS WITHOUT ANY SLEEP TO FINISH THIS REPORT.

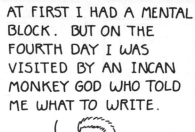

AT FIRST I HAD A MENTAL BLOCK. BUT ON THE FOURTH DAY I WAS VISITED BY AN INCAN MONKEY GOD WHO TOLD ME WHAT TO WRITE.

8-3

WOW, LUCKY BREAK.

NOW I JUST HAVE TO FIND SOMEBODY WHO CAN TRANSLATE HIS SIMPLE BUT BEAUTIFUL LANGUAGE.

I'VE SACRIFICED MY HEALTH, MY PERSONAL LIFE AND MY SOUL TO GET PROMOTED.

HA HA HA! BUT IT WAS ALL WORTH IT BECAUSE I HAVE AN OFFICE WITH A <u>DOOR</u> AND YOU STILL <u>WORK</u> IN A CUBICLE!

MAYBE I'LL HOST A SPECIAL "LOW-ACHIEVER DAY" TO LET YOU TOUCH MY DOOR.

OOPS

THANK YOU ALL FOR COMING. THERE'S NO SPECIFIC AGENDA FOR THIS MEETING...

AS USUAL, WE'LL JUST MAKE UNRELATED EMOTIONAL STATEMENTS ABOUT THINGS WHICH BOTHER US. I'LL KICK IT OFF...

THERE'S NEVER TIME TO GET ANY WORK DONE AROUND HERE!!

HEY, I HAVEN'T DONE A THING FOR MINUTES AND YET I STILL GET PAID.

HOO-HOO-HA! I'M RIPPING OFF THE EVIL CORPORATE EMPIRE AND THERE'S NOTHING THEY CAN DO ABOUT IT! I HAVE TOTAL POWER!

I'D BETTER KEEP THIS LITTLE SECRET TO MYSELF.

HEY, I'M GETTING PAID FOR DOING NOTHING!

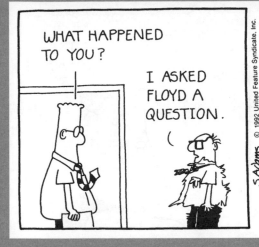

WHAT HAPPENED TO YOU?

I ASKED FLOYD A QUESTION.

FLOYD HATES HIS JOB, SO HE TAKES IT OUT ON CO-WORKERS. HE ALMOST CHEWED MY CLOTHES OFF.

HOW'D YOU STOP HIM?

HE WENT INTO SYNTHETIC SHOCK; IT'S NOT HEALTHY TO EAT TOO MUCH OF THIS STUFF.

WHAT?! YOU THINK I'LL HELP YOU JUST BECAUSE I'M YOUR CO-WORKER?? HA! I HATE CO-WORKERS!

ALL I NEED IS...

I HATE THIS JOB! I HATE EVERYTHING! THE ONLY THING I LIKE IS BEING MEAN TO CO-WORKERS WHO NEED THE VITAL INFORMATION THAT I CONTROL!

IF YOU THINK YOU HATE HIM, YOU SHOULD TRY BEING HIS SECRETARY.

EVERYBODY PICK A STRAW. THE LOSER HAS TO KILL OUR ABUSIVE CO-WORKER, FLOYD.

DILBERT LOSES. HE PICKED THE BLUE STRAW.

I THOUGHT THE SHORT STRAW LOSES.

YOU'RE ALREADY A MURDERER; DON'T BE A CHEATER TOO.

THE GUYS IN THE OFFICE DECIDED THAT SOMEBODY MUST KILL FLOYD THE BUDGET MANAGER BECAUSE HE'S SO MEAN TO US.

THEY WANT ME TO KILL HIM. BUT I CAN'T DO IT. I'M A LOVER, NOT A KILLER.

TECHNICALLY, YOU'RE NEITHER.

IS THAT MY FAULT?

I'VE GOT TO TELL YOU, FLOYD, THAT YOUR CO-WORKERS ARE SO FED UP WITH YOUR ATTITUDE THAT THEY ASKED ME TO ... UH... KILL YOU.

WHAT??!

HEH-HEH... OF COURSE THERE'S NO WAY I'D ACTUALLY...

ERK! MMPH...

I'M REALLY GOING TO HAVE TO DRESS THIS UP ON MY QUARTERLY ACCOMPLISHMENT REPORT.

WE HEARD YOU KILLED FLOYD, OUR UNBEARABLE CO-WORKER, YESTERDAY.

NO. I WAS THERE, BUT HE CHOKED ON HIS OWN BILE.

WHAT DID YOU DO – PERFORM FIRST AID? CALL AN AMBULANCE?

I DON'T KNOW FIRST AID.

UH... CAN I USE YOUR PHONE?

WHAT'S THE STORY WITH THE COSTUME, WALLY?

THE BOSS PUT ME ON A SPECIAL TASK FORCE TO SEE IF HUMOR INCREASES CREATIVITY. I HAVE TO DRESS LIKE THIS FOR A MONTH.

12-10

ARE YOU FEELING MORE CREATIVE?

YEAH. I'VE ALREADY THOUGHT OF SIX HUNDRED WAYS TO KILL HIM.

SO... DILBERT, WELCOME TO THE SALES DEPARTMENT. I'M TINA, YOUR NEW BOSS.

HI

AS THE NEW GUY, YOU GET THE CUSTOMERS WHO DESPISE OUR PRODUCTS AND WANT TO HURT US PERSONALLY.

12-15

I HATE YOU! I HATE YOU!

YOU'LL BE SELLING TO THE SMALL BUSINESS MARKET. HE'S YOUR BEST ACCOUNT.

AS PART OF MY PROGRAM TO USE MORE HUMOR AT WORK, I'M ASKING EACH OF YOU TO WEAR A "KICK ME" SIGN.

KICK ME

12-11

I'LL CHECK LATER TO SEE IF YOU'RE MORE RELAXED AND CREATIVE.

KICK ME

LATER...

YOU SEEM TO BE TAKING UNFAIR ADVANTAGE OF THE SITUATION, ALICE.

DOGBERT IS A CREATIVITY CONSULTANT

WE DON'T NEED ANY OF YOUR "INTUITION" MUMBO JUMBO. WE NEED QUANTITATIVE DATA!

THE ONLY WAY TO MAKE DECISIONS IS TO PULL NUMBERS OUT OF THE AIR, CALL THEM "ASSUMPTIONS," AND CALCULATE THE NET PRESENT VALUE.

OF COURSE, YOU HAVE TO USE THE RIGHT DISCOUNT RATE, OTHERWISE IT'S MEANINGLESS.

GO AWAY.

WHAT ARE YOU UP TO, TED?

I'M WORKING LIKE A DOG LATELY.

I'D BETTER NOT ASK.

SCRATCH SCRATCH

I'VE GOT GOOD NEWS AND BAD NEWS.

THE BAD NEWS IS THAT HUGE COMPANIES LIKE US CAN'T COMPETE AGAINST SMALL, NIMBLE COMPANIES. THE GOOD NEWS IS THAT AT THIS RATE WE'LL BE THE SMALLEST COMPANY AROUND.

WHAT AM I DOING WRONG HERE?

WE'RE NUMBER ONE!

WE'RE NUMBER ONE!

YES!!

HEY, WALLY, HOW DID YOU GET A ROOF FOR YOUR CUBICLE?

THIS STUFF IS ALL MODULAR. YOU JUST TAKE SOME IDIOT'S WALL AND MAKE IT YOUR CEILING.

BY ANY CHANCE, DO YOU KNOW WHAT HAPPENED TO MY WALL?

WHAT DID IT LOOK LIKE?

I'VE BEEN SAYING FOR YEARS THAT "EMPLOYEES ARE OUR MOST VALUABLE ASSET."

IT TURNS OUT THAT I WAS WRONG. MONEY IS OUR MOST VALUABLE ASSET. EMPLOYEES ARE NINTH.

I'M AFRAID TO ASK WHAT CAME IN EIGHTH.

CARBON PAPER.

LOOK EVERYONE, I'M ENGAGED!

HEY, IT'S ONE OF THOSE "NEAR DIAMOND" RINGS THEY WERE SELLING ON THE TV SHOPPING CHANNEL FOR $29.95.

UH... OF COURSE IT HAS A LIST PRICE OF OVER A HUNDRED DOLLARS...

OOH, GOOD SAVE.

A SMALL BAND OF THE CREATURES WERE KNOWN TO LIVE HIGH IN AN ARTIFICIAL STRUCTURE.

ON MY WAY TO STUDY THEM I TOOK NOTE OF THE NATIVE VEGETATION.

RENTED

THE YOUNGER MALES WERE AT PLAY. THEY BECAME SELF-CONSCIOUS WHEN WATCHED.

THE DOMINANT MALE HAD A GRAY BACK. HE CONTROLLED THE OTHERS BY WAVING LITTLE ENVELOPES.

THERE WERE FEW FEMALES IN THE GROUP. THE LESS DOMINANT MALES HAD NO CHANCE OF MATING.

UNLIKE OTHER SPECIES THEY HAD NO INSTINCT FOR GROOMING.

WANT TO GROOM?

DROP DEAD.

4-11

MY TIME WAS UP. BUT I WILL MISS THEM, THOSE...

ENGINEERS IN THE MIST

HOW LONG ARE YOU SUPPOSED TO MICROWAVE POPCORN?

I'M SO MAD... I JUST BOUGHT A NEW COMPUTER AND IT'S ALREADY OBSOLETE.

DON'T FEEL BAD. THE OTHER ENGINEERS WON'T LOOK DOWN ON YOU JUST BECAUSE YOU'RE BEHIND THE TECHNOLOGY CURVE.

YEAH, WE WILL.

NOT RIGHT IN FRONT OF HIM.

DON'T GET TOO CLOSE-- I FOUND OUT THAT MY BALDNESS IS CAUSED BY TOO MUCH TESTOSTERONE.

NOW WITH MY HAIR GONE I'M AFRAID THE TESTOSTERONE WILL START FLINGING OUT OF MY PORES.

HEY! YOU GOT SOME ON MY SHIRT!

DO YOU HAVE A PROBLEM WITH THAT?

GEE, WALLY, YOU SURE HAVE BEEN POPULAR WITH WOMEN SINCE THE TESTOSTERONE STARTED SPEWING FROM YOUR HEAD.

IT'S AMAZING... I EVEN BOUGHT A PICKUP TRUCK AND A RIFLE SO I CAN HUNT AFTER WORK.

WHAT DO YOU HUNT AROUND HERE?

PIGEONS ARE THE MOST CONVENIENT... DON'T EVEN HAVE TO GET OUT OF THE TRUCK.

DILBERT IS ASSIGNED TO PREPARE THE BUDGET.

YOU'LL HAVE TO LEARN OUR BUDGET SYSTEM.

IT WAS DEVELOPED 400 YEARS AGO BY A CRAZED MONK WHO SEALED HIMSELF IN A WINE CASK.

5-11

UNFORTUNATELY, WE STILL HAVE HIM.

HEY, I'VE GOT ANOTHER IDEA.

THE OTHER ENGINEERS SHUN ME BECAUSE I'M ASSIGNED TO WORK ON THE BUDGET.

SHUN

5-12

THEY KNOW I COULD POUNCE ANY MOMENT AND ASK INANE HYPOTHETICAL BUDGET QUESTIONS.

SHUN

WHAT IF YOU ONLY HAD HALF AS MUCH ELECTRICITY NEXT YEAR?

TOO LATE. I SHUNNED YOU.

HEY, "DIL-BUTT," I HEAR THEY GOT YOU DOING BUDGET WORK NOW.

HA HA! IT MUST BE REALLY EXCITING WORK. I MEAN, GOSH, MAKING ALL THOSE NUMBERS ADD UP.

5-13

HA HA! I'M GLAD I HAVE A REAL JOB!

NOT ANYMORE.

CLICK

...COMPANIES MUST LEARN TO EMBRACE CHANGE.

UH-OH. IT'S ANOTHER MANAGEMENT FAD.

WILL IT PASS QUICKLY OR WILL IT LINGER LIKE THE STENCH OF A DEAD WOODCHUCK UNDER THE PORCH?

5-4

I THINK WE SHOULD DO A "CHANGE" NEWSLETTER.

WOODCHUCK.

© 1993 United Feature Syndicate, Inc.

MY PRODUCTIVITY IS SHOT. I CAN'T STOP DAYDREAMING ABOUT IRENE IN ACCOUNTING.

5-25   S. Adams

DO WHAT I DID. TRY TO PHASE OUT OF IT BY DAYDREAMING OF LAURA IN ENGINEERING, THEN MOVE TO THE ORDINARY-LOOKING BETTY IN MARKETING.

© 1993 United Feature Syndicate, Inc.

NOW I'M DAYDREAMING ABOUT ALL THREE OF THEM.

SAME THING HAPPENED TO ME.

I UNDERSTAND THAT YOU MEN ARE SPENDING THREE-QUARTERS OF YOUR TIME DAYDREAMING ABOUT ATTRACTIVE WOMEN.

DO YOU REALIZE HOW MUCH TIME IS BEING WASTED HERE?

S. Adams

© 1993 United Feature Syndicate, Inc.

TWENTY-FIVE PERCENT?

IT'S A TRICK QUESTION.

IRENE

5-26

MY "DEFANTALATOR" INVENTION CAN ELIMINATE THE UNPRODUCTIVE AND NAUGHTY THOUGHTS OF YOUR MALE EMPLOYEES.

WE SUCCEEDED IN GETTING MEN TO STOP <u>ACTING</u> LIKE MEN, BUT IT WASN'T ENOUGH. MEN MUST STOP <u>THINKING</u> LIKE MEN TOO.

5-27

HEY! CUT IT OUT!

HMM... A LITTLE MAKE-UP AND A NEW HAIR-DO...

THERE'S ANOTHER UNPRODUCTIVE MAN, DAYDREAMING ABOUT ATTRACTIVE WOMEN.

A SHORT BURST FROM MY "DE-FANTALATOR" SHOULD SET HIM STRAIGHT.

WUSSS

5-28

HEY! I THINK I'M STARTING TO LIKE FIGURE SKATING!

I TOOK A CRACK AT WRITING A "MISSION STATEMENT" FOR OUR GROUP.

"WE ENHANCE STOCK-HOLDER VALUE THROUGH STRATEGIC BUSINESS INITIATIVES BY EMPOWERED EMPLOYEES WORKING IN NEW TEAM PARADIGMS."

6-14

DO YOU EVER JUST MARVEL AT THE FACT WE GET PAID TO DO THIS?

DID ANY-BODY BRING DONUTS?

MANY OF YOU COME TO MY MANAGEMENT SEMINAR AS OPTIMISTIC, CREATIVE, CLEAR-SPEAKING INDIVIDUALS.

BUT WITH HARD WORK, YOU CAN BECOME JARGON-SPEWING CORPORATE ZOMBIES, LIKE CARL HERE.

I WANT TO DIALOGUE WITH YOU ABOUT UTILIZING RESOURCES.

GOOD BOY! HERE'S A DONUT.

AS YOU KNOW, ALL PROJECTS ARE ASSIGNED ACRONYMS. UNFORTUNATELY, ALL THE GOOD ONES HAVE BEEN USED.

ANY NEW PROJECT WILL HAVE TO USE AN ACRONYM FROM THIS SHORT LIST OF SOMEWHAT LESS DESIRABLE CHOICES.

WHAT SHOULD I CALL MY NEW PROJECT?

WELL, YOU COULD USE "PHLEGM" OR "PLACENTA."

MY PATENT APPLICATION IS COMPLETE. SOON THE OTHER ENGINEERS WILL COME SNIFFING AROUND.

THEY ARE ATTRACTED BY THE SCENT OF SUCCESS. THEY WANT THEIR NAMES ON MY PATENT.

THE SCENT CAN'T BE COMING FROM HERE.

WE MAY BE GETTING A FALSE POSITIVE FROM HIS BALONEY SANDWICH.

DILBERT, WOULD YOU ADD MY NAME TO YOUR PATENT APPLICATION?

WHY SHOULD I?

I WOULD CONSIDER UPGRADING YOUR STATUS FROM "CO-WORKER" TO "FRIEND I NEVER SEE OUTSIDE OF WORK."

WOULD WE EAT LUNCH TOGETHER?

NO, BUT I'LL PENCIL YOU IN AND CANCEL AT THE LAST MINUTE.

LET'S START WITH A BRAINSTORMING EXERCISE. ALICE, YOU GO FIRST.

I IMAGINE MYSELF NOT SURROUNDED BY DULL, UNATTRACTIVE, AND LARGELY CLUELESS MEN.

I THINK SHE JUST INSULTED YOU GUYS.

MMMM...

ALICE, MARY, LET'S GO TO THE LADIES ROOM!

I RENTED "GONE WITH THE WIND." WE CAN WATCH IT ON THE BIG SCREEN TV

I WANT THE GREY SOFA!

HEY, LOOK! THE MEN'S ROOM HAS SOAP!!

59

I'VE GOT TO CUT STAFF IN ENGINEERING. I'M TRYING TO DETERMINE WHICH ONE OF YOU IS MORE VALUABLE TO KEEP.

I'VE BEEN HEARING GOOD THINGS ABOUT ZIMBU THE MONKEY. WHICH ONE OF YOU IS ZIMBU THE MONKEY?

THIS IS NOT THE PROUDEST MOMENT OF MY PROFESSIONAL CAREER.

I'M TOLD BY A RELIABLE SOURCE THAT OUR SENIOR VICE PRESIDENT MADE A SOUND LIKE "YURP" AT LUNCH.

WHAT DOES IT MEAN? DOES IT SIGNAL A NEW SET OF PRIORITIES? WE MUST DEMONSTRATE OUR COMMITMENT TO THIS VISION.

WHAT WAS THE CONTEXT OF THIS VISION?

ALL WE KNOW IS HE WAS EATING A BURRITO.

I'LL GIVE ALBERT A MALE BONDING SHOULDER MASSAGE TO SHOW I'M A TEAM PLAYER.

HEY, AL! KEEP UP THE GOOD WORK, BUDDY!

OOPS... THAT MIGHT HAVE BEEN THE VULCAN DEATH GRIP.

60

HAVE I TOLD YOU RECENTLY THAT I HAVE A LUCRATIVE JOB OFFER FROM OUR COMPETITOR?

YES

THE PAY IS OBSCENE, THEY WEAR CASUAL CLOTHES AT WORK, AND WEDNESDAY THROUGH FRIDAY IS FREE BEER AND PIZZA.

AS THE NEW GUY I GET TO DATE THE MASSEUSE UNTIL THE COMPANY MATCHES ME WITH AN ATTRACTIVE CO-WORKER.

SOB%

NEXT WEEK I'LL BE AT MY NEW JOB, REAPING HUGE REWARDS.

WE'RE SO HAPPY FOR YOU.

BUT I'LL STILL HAVE A LITTLE CUBICLE LIKE YOURS.

THE ONLY DIFFERENCE BEING THAT I'LL KEEP A PONY THERE. THAT WAY IT'S CLOSE TO MY OFFICE.

I CAN'T KEEP WORKING THESE LONG HOURS... I DESERVE A FAMILY LIFE.

ALICE, ALICE, ALICE...

THIS ISN'T THE "ME" GENERATION OF THE EIGHTIES. THIS IS THE "LIFELESS NINETIES." I EXPECT 178 HOURS OF WORK FROM YOU EACH WEEK.

THERE ARE ONLY... UH, 168 HOURS IN A WEEK.

I EXPECT YOUR FAMILY TO CHIP IN A FEW HOURS.

I'M WORKING TOO MANY HOURS... I NEVER SPEND TIME WITH MY FAMILY.

THE COMPANY CARES. THAT'S WHY WE'VE DEVELOPED A PROGRAM TO TEACH YOU HOW TO COPE.

"CELIBACY AND ADOPTION — THE CHOICE FOR THE NINETIES."

I NEED TO IDENTIFY ANY UNNECESSARY AND UNPRODUCTIVE EMPLOYEES SO I CAN CUT COSTS.

DOES ANYBODY HAVE SPARE TIME TO JOIN MY TASK FORCE ON PRODUCTIVITY?

GOOD, GOOD... ANYBODY ELSE?

HOO-BOY! I HOPE YOU'RE NOT GOING TO SHOW THIS TO ANYBODY.

OH, IT'S OBVIOUSLY A FIRST DRAFT. BY NOW YOU'VE RUN IT THROUGH THE SPELLING CHECKER.

TECHNOLOGISTS ARE CONCERNED WITH IDEAS, NOT SPELLING.

WELL, SINCE YOU BROUGHT IT UP...

ONE OF THESE DONUTS CONTAINS A MEMO WHICH FIRES THE RECIPIENT.

THIS SEEMED LIKE THE MOST HUMANE WAY TO REDUCE HEAD COUNT.

HOW WAS YOUR DONUT?

THE FIRST TWO WERE GREAT. THE THIRD WAS PAPERY.

© 1994 United Feature Syndicate, Inc.

MAY I SLIP IN? I ONLY NEED ONE COPY.

WHAT'S THE MESSAGE HERE? IS YOUR TIME WORTH MORE THAN MY TIME BECAUSE YOU'RE A MANAGER AND I'M A SECRETARY? HUH?

THIS MIGHT STING FOR A SECOND, BUT IT'LL REMOVE YOUR DESIRE TO MAKE COPIES.

© 1993 United Feature Syndicate, Inc.

11-24

THE "SECRETARY WITH A CROSSBOW" GOES ON THE HUNT.

MOBY DICK!

© 1993 United Feature Syndicate, Inc.

YOU'VE BEEN HARPOONED AGAIN, SIR.

YEAH, BUT I CAPSIZED HER DESK.

11-25

DILBERT THE MENTOR

THIS IS YOUR COMPUTER.

WHEN YOU HEAR FOOTSTEPS IT'S A GOOD IDEA TO MOVE THIS THING AROUND AND CLICK IT.

THIS CONCLUDES YOUR TECHNICAL TRAINING. IF YOU HAVE FURTHER QUESTIONS JUST REMEMBER YOU'RE INCONVENIENCING ME.

IT'S "PHIL, THE PRINCE OF INSUFFICIENT LIGHT"!

I SAW YOU TAKE THAT CHAIR.

I SUMMON ALL THE DEMONS AND TROLLS OF HECK TO COME FORTH AND PUNISH YOU NOW!!!

I'M ED, FROM ACCOUNTING. THE OTHERS ARE AT LUNCH.

IF THE WAREHOUSE WON'T REPLACE MY BROKEN CHAIR, I'LL JUST TAKE ONE FROM SOMEBODY. ELSE.

TECHNICALLY, IT'S NOT STEALING BECAUSE THE CHAIR BELONGS TO THE COMPANY EITHER WAY.

WHAT'S THE WORST THING THAT COULD HAPPEN?

HOLD THE ELEVATOR. ...OVER.

66

TODAY YOU WILL LEARN HOW TO DEAL WITH PEOPLE WHO HAVE PERSONALITY DEFECTS.

S. Adams

CASE 1: TODD LAUGHS NERVOUSLY AT EVERY ONE OF HIS OWN COMMENTS.

DON'T HOLD IT AGAINST ME! HEE HEE HAW HAW!

REMEDY: TODD MUST BE RELOCATED TO A DISTANT PLANET.

IT SURE IS LONELY! HEE HEE!

CASE 2: ALLEN STARES AT YOU LIKE A ZOMBIE FOR LONG PERIODS BEFORE RESPONDING TO QUESTIONS.

REMEDY: ALLEN MUST BE PAIRED WITH VIRGINIA (CASE 3) WHO FILLS ALL QUIET SPOTS WITH INANE CHATTER.

YAK YAK YAK

© 1993 United Feature Syndicate, Inc.

CASE 4: MATT SPEAKS SLOWLY ABOUT AMAZINGLY BORING TOPICS.

I... ATE... A ...PICKLE...

12-12

REMEDY: MATT'S HEAD CAN BE OUTFITTED WITH A READING STAND.

I... LIKE... PICKLES...

CASE 5: AN ENGINEER. REMEDY: VERY QUIETLY SEAL HIM IN HIS OWN CUBICLE.

I...I'D LIKE PERMISSION TO KEEP A PLASTIC PLANT IN MY CUBICLE.

CUBICLE GESTAPO

1-17

PERMISSION DENIED! PLANTS ATTRACT BUGS. IF I CAN'T TELL IT'S PLASTIC HOW ARE THE BUGS GOING TO KNOW THE DIFFERENCE?

WITH ALL DUE RESPECT, BUGS ARE WAY SMARTER THAN YOU.

OH YEAH? I'D LIKE TO SEE THEM DO THIS JOB.

© 1994 United Feature Syndicate, Inc.

HERE'S YOUR "BUZZWORD BINGO" CARD FOR THE MEETING.

2-22

IF THE BOSS USES A BUZZWORD ON YOUR CARD, YOU CHECK IT OFF. THE OBJECTIVE IS TO FILL A ROW.

© 1994 United Feature Syndicate, Inc.

YOU'RE ALL VERY ATTENTIVE TODAY. MY PROACTIVE LEADERSHIP MUST BE WORKING!

BINGO, SIR.

ZIMBU THE MONKEY DESIGNED THREE COMMERCIAL PRODUCTS THIS WEEK! WE'D BETTER FIND OUT HIS SECRET.

3-28

HE'S USING HIS TAIL! HE HAS A NATURAL ADVANTAGE!

© 1994 United Feature Syndicate, Inc.

I FEEL THE JAWS OF EVOLUTION ON MY THROAT.

GOOD GRAVY! DID YOU SEE HIM CUT AND PASTE?!

ZIMBU, YOU'RE NOT SUPPOSED TO USE YOUR TAIL TO OPERATE THE MOUSE.

IF TAILS WERE A NATURAL ADVANTAGE FOR ENGINEERS THEN EVOLUTION WOULD PROVIDE US ALL WITH TAILS!

3-30

DILBERT, I DON'T BELIEVE YOU'VE MET ROCKY, OUR NEW C PROGRAMMER.

EVOLUTION FAVORS MONKEYS. EVENTUALLY, HUMANS WILL BE KEPT IN CAGES AS PETS

BAH!

IMPOSSIBLE! WE HUMANS WILL NEVER ALLOW OURSELVES TO BE TREATED LIKE THAT!

4-1

NOW GET OUT OF MY CUBICLE!

TELL ME ABOUT YOUR PROJECT AND I'LL TRANSLATE IT INTO WEASEL WORDS FOR THE BUSINESS CASE.

WELL... AN EXECUTIVE HAD LUNCH WITH A VENDOR AND COMMITTED TO BUY SOME STUFF THAT DOESN'T WORK. OUR JOB IS TO COST-JUSTIFY THE DECISION.

4-13

I QUIT.

DON'T GET ALL ETHICAL ON US.

70

I CAN'T BELIEVE WE HAVE TO GO TO "DIVERSITY SENSITIVITY" TRAINING.

WALLY, I DON'T SEE HOW IT COULD BE BAD TO SEEK A BETTER UNDERSTANDING OF OTHERS.

UH-OH

TAKE A SEAT IN THE "DUMPY WHITE GUY SECTION." I'M READY TO START.

IN THIS SENSITIVITY EXERCISE, CLOSE YOUR EYES AND IMAGINE HOW IT FEELS TO BE A WOMAN.

PEOPLE ACKNOWLEDGE MY EXISTENCE. THEY SMILE FOR NO REASON AND HOLD THE DOOR OPEN. I'M... I'M POPULAR.

I CAN'T FIND MY KEYS.

I'M NEVER GOING BACK. I CAN'T. I WON'T.

MY BLOUSE FALLS TO THE FLOOR...

BREAK! BREAK!

THE COMPANY CARES DEEPLY ABOUT THE EFFECTS OF LONG HOURS AND STRESS ON THE WORKERS.

SO THEY'RE PAYING NEARLY $200 TO HAVE AN EXPERT ON STRESS-REDUCTION GIVE A TALK DURING LUNCH.

JUST WHEN YOU THINK THEY DON'T CARE, SOMETHING LIKE THIS COMES ALONG.

IT'S SCHEDULED FOR LAST TUESDAY.

I GUESS IT'S TIME TO GO BACK TO MY DIMLY LIT CUBICLE AND SEE IF MY CARPAL TUNNEL HAS CRIPPLED ME YET.

THIS IS A LOT LIKE MY LAST JOB AS A COAL MINER, BUT WITHOUT THE THREAT OF A GAS EXPLOSION.

7-16

I'M MOVING YOU TO A NEW CUBICLE OVER BY WALLY.

BETTER GET A CANARY.

© 1994 United Feature Syndicate, Inc.

OUR CEO CANCELLED HIS VISIT. HE'S SENDING HIS TOP AID, ZIMBU THE MONKEY, IN HIS PLACE.

ISN'T THAT TYPICAL? I SPENT A WEEK EXAGGERATING MY ACCOMPLISHMENTS FOR THIS. NOW HE SENDS A STUPID MONKEY!

7-30 © 1994 United Feature Syndicate, Inc.

WHAT COULD BE MORE HUMILIATING THAN TRYING TO SUCK-UP TO A MONKEY?

FAILING AT IT?

THIS WILL BE A TOUGH YEAR FOR THE COMPANY.

IT WILL TAKE A SPECIAL KIND OF TEAM TO GET BY.

© 1994 United Feature Syndicate, Inc.

GO TEAM!

TEAM! TEAM!

YES!

SPECIFICALLY, IT WILL TAKE A MUCH SMALLER TEAM.

8-11

I'M RUNNING LATE. BUT SINCE I'M A VICE PRESIDENT YOU'LL HAVE TO WAIT IN THE HALLWAY.

YOU'LL BE ABLE TO JUDGE YOUR RELATIVE WORTH BY OBSERVING WHAT THINGS I DO WHILE YOU WAIT.

9-27

HE'S TEACHING HIMSELF THE BANJO.

THIS CARTOON SEEMS TO BE SAYING THAT MANAGEMENT DECISIONS ARE A JOKE.

CARTOONS ARE NOT ALLOWED ON CUBICLES. IT HURTS MORALE. I DON'T WANT TO SEE THIS WHEN I RETURN.

9-28

I'VE NOTICED A REAL IMPROVEMENT IN MORALE SINCE YOU REMOVED THE CARTOON.

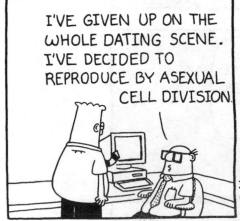

I'VE GIVEN UP ON THE WHOLE DATING SCENE. I'VE DECIDED TO REPRODUCE BY ASEXUAL CELL DIVISION.

I DIDN'T REALIZE THAT WAS AN OPTION.

YOU NEVER KNOW UNTIL YOU TRY.

I THINK I'LL STEER CLEAR OF HERE FOR A WHILE.

DIVIDE! DIVIDE!

10-15

76

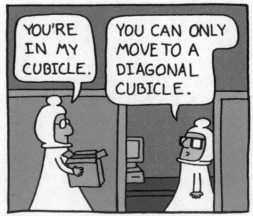

THIS JOB HAS TAKEN MY DIGNITY, MY SELF-ESTEEM, MY CREATIVITY AND MY PRECIOUS TIME ON THIS EARTH.

YOU'VE TAKEN ALL I HAVE! THERE'S NOTHING LEFT TO GIVE!!!

THE BLOOD DRIVE IS NEXT WEEK. THIS YEAR IT'S MANDATORY... AND A THREE-PINT MINIMUM.

... AND IF I PILE ENOUGH BINDERS ON MY CHAIR I'LL HAVE A WINDOW VIEW!

I'VE GOT TO TRY THAT.

WOW! I'VE NEVER SEEN SO MUCH INTEREST IN OUR BUSINESS PLAN!

CAN I HAVE TWO?

ONE OF THESE DONUTS CONTAINS A MEMO WHICH FIRES THE RECIPIENT.

THIS SEEMED LIKE THE MOST HUMANE WAY TO REDUCE HEAD COUNT.

HOW WAS YOUR DONUT?

THE FIRST TWO WERE GREAT. THE THIRD WAS PAPERY.

WE'RE WAITING FOR TED, THEN WE CAN HEAD FOR THE RESTAURANT.

WHILE WE'RE WAITING, I'LL RETURN A FEW PHONE CALLS.

LET'S GO! HEY, WHERE'S WALLY?

THE CHAIN REACTION HAS BEGUN.

WHY CAN'T WE DO THIS SIMPLE THING?

I'LL BE IN THE LADIES ROOM.

WHERE'S ALICE?

I'VE GOT TO MAIL A LETTER. I'LL TAKE MY CAR AND MEET YOU THERE.

I CAN MAKE SOME CALLS.

YOU'RE THE ONLY ONE WHO KNOWS WHICH RESTAURANT WE'RE GOING TO!

ALICE KNOWS WHERE IT IS. TELL HER IT'S THE ONE WITH THE FOOD.

HAS YOUR TEAM FINISHED ENGINEERING THE NEW MISSILE GUIDANCE CHIP?

I THINK IT'S TIME TO GIVE PEACE A CHANCE.

IT'S SEVEN O'CLOCK, ED. TIME TO CALL IT A NIGHT.

I'M PLANNING TO WORK ALL NIGHT.

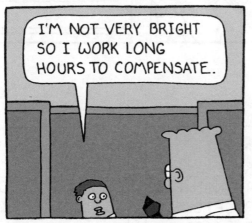

I'M NOT VERY BRIGHT SO I WORK LONG HOURS TO COMPENSATE.

ED, WE'RE NOT BETTER OFF WHEN YOU DO EXTRA WORK.

I'M NOT QUITE FOLLOWING YOUR LOGIC.

WE ALL WORKED LATE UNDOING WHAT YOU DID YESTERDAY.

WE VOTED TO DUCT-TAPE YOU TO YOUR CHAIR.

IT'S UNCANNY HOW MANY PROBLEMS YOU CAN SOLVE WITH DUCT TAPE.

SOMETIMES I USE IT INSTEAD OF UNDER-WEAR.

LOOK, TED! WE GET PAID THE SAME AS YOU BUT ALL WE'RE DOING IS STANDING AROUND AND FLICKING OUR FINGERS.

COME JOIN US AND FLICK YOUR FINGERS IN JOYOUS CELEBRATION THAT OUR PERFORMANCE IS NOT LINKED TO OUR PAY.

FLICK FLICK

I DON'T KNOW WHAT SUCCESS SOUNDS LIKE, BUT I'LL BET THIS ISN'T IT.

FLICK FLICK FLICK FLICK FLICK

EXCUSE ME... I'M ONLY AN INTERN, BUT MAY I MAKE A SUGGESTION?

LET'S FORM MULTI-DISCIPLINARY TASK FORCES TO REENGINEER OUR CORE PROCESSES UNTIL WE'RE A WORLD CLASS ORGANIZATION!

SOUNDS GOOD. GO DO IT.

I'M MORE OF AN IDEA RAT.

ACCORDING TO YOU, IF I CUT YOUR BUDGET THE WORLD WILL ABRUPTLY STOP SPINNING AND WE'LL BE FLUNG INTO SPACE.

WHEREAS, THE RISK OF CUTTING DILBERT'S PROJECT IS "...A PLAGUE OF LOCUSTS O'ER THE LAND."

I'LL CUT BOTH PROJECTS. WITH ANY LUCK, WE'LL FLING THE LOCUSTS INTO SPACE.

LOCUSTS. REAL GOOD.

BE AT THE "UNITED CHARITY" KICKOFF TOMORROW.

I HIRED A HEADLESS MAN TO BE OUR INSPIRATIONAL SPEAKER.

...AND THAT'S HOW "UNITED CHARITY" GAVE ME BACK MY DIGNITY. ANY QUESTIONS?

HOW DO YOU SHOW UP ON A HEADCOUNT REPORT?

NOW THAT WE DON'T HAVE OUR OWN CUBICLES I HAVE TO KEEP MY BINDERS IN THIS SHOPPING CART.

AND I'VE DEVELOPED A STRONG INTEREST IN GRAFFITI AS A WAY TO EXPRESS MY INDIVIDUALITY.

WELL... IT COULD BE WORSE.

I'M THINKING OF JOINING A GANG.

I CAN'T DECIDE IF I SHOULD STAY WITH ENGINEERING OR PURSUE A CAREER IN MANAGEMENT.

IN MY HEART I'M AN ENGINEER BUT I HEAR A VOICE CALLING ME TO THE DARK SIDE.

I FOUND YOUR PROBLEM.

BOY IS MY FACE RED.

I'M DRESSING LIKE A MAN TO PROTEST THE COMPANY'S DRESS CODE.

SO, WHAT YOU'RE SAYING IS THAT YOU'RE ACTUALLY A WOMAN. IS THAT YOUR CLAIM?

THAT'S NOT EXACTLY THE POINT.

I SAW "THE CRYING GAME." DON'T DO ANYTHING THAT WOULD MAKE ME HEAVE.

2/10

WHEN YOU CONSIDER THE HOURS I WORK, I MAKE LESS PER HOUR THAN THE JANITOR!

LOOK WHAT WAS BLOCKING THE PIPES! IT TOOK ME ALL MORNING TO PLUNGE THE RASCAL OUT.

I LOVE MY JOB.

I'M GIVING HIM A RAISE.

2/16

I WAS SO LATE I HAD TO PUT ON MY MAKEUP IN THE CAR.

YEAH, I HAD TO SHAVE IN THE CAR.

THAT'S NOTHING. I WAS SO LATE THAT I HAD TO GIVE MYSELF A SPONGE BATH IN THE CAR.

AREN'T YOU THE DRIVER FOR YOUR CARPOOL?

YOU'VE NEVER HEARD SUCH WHINING.

BOSS TYPES

FIND YOUR BOSS ON THIS HANDY REFERENCE.

S. ADAMS

HOSTAGE TAKER: TRAPS YOU IN YOUR CUBICLE AND TALKS YOUR EARS OFF.

BLAH BLAH

OW!!

FRAUD: USES VIGOROUS HEAD-NODDING TO SIMULATE COMPREHENSION.

THEN WE'LL SUBNET OUR I.P. ADDRESSES.

OH YEAH OH YEAH

MOTIVATIONAL LIAR: HAS NO CLUE WHAT YOU DO BUT SAYS YOU'RE THE BEST.

NOBODY CAN DO WHAT YOU DO!!

EXCEPT A MUSHROOM.

OVER PROMOTED: TRIES TO MASK INCOMPETENCE WITH POOR COMMUNICATION.

LET'S QUALITIZE OUR PARADIGM SO WE DON'T OVER INUNDATE WITH DATUMS.

© 1995 United Feature Syndicate, Inc.

WEASEL: TAKES CREDIT FOR YOUR HARD WORK.

THIS BONUS IS FOR BRILLIANTLY FORCING YOUR STAFF TO WORK 80 HOUR WEEKS.

IT WASN'T EASY!

2-19

MOSES: PERPETUALLY WAITS FOR CLEAR SIGNALS FROM ABOVE.

DON'T DO ANYTHING IMPORTANT YET.

NEVER HAVE.

PERFECT BOSS: DIES OF NATURAL CAUSES ON A THURSDAY AFTERNOON.

SHOULD WE DO SOMETHING?

THREE DAY WEEKEND!

RELIABLE SOURCES SAY YOUR PROJECT WILL BE CANCELLED, DILBERT.

2/20

YOU SHOULD ABANDON IT NOW AND COME WORK ON MY PROJECT. WHEN MY BIG PROMOTION GOES THROUGH NEXT MONTH, I'LL TRANSFER YOU TO MY GROUP AND GIVE YOU A RAISE.

THAT'S VERY TEMPTING EXCEPT FOR THE FACT YOU'RE A PATHOLOGICAL LIAR.

BE CAREFUL WHAT YOU SAY - I HAVE SUPER POWERS.

ALICE, I'M ALMOST DONE WITH YOUR PERFORMANCE APPRAISAL.

GASP

I HAVEN'T HAD AN APPRAISAL IN FOUR YEARS. YOU MUST BE STARTING A DOCUMENTATION TRAIL SO YOU CAN FIRE ME LATER.

2/23

I'LL WORK 24 HOURS A DAY!!

THAT WAS WAY MORE MOTIVATIONAL THAN I'D HOPED.

I'M TERRIFIED ABOUT MY PERFORMANCE REVIEW TOMORROW.

2/24

MEN HAVE IT EASIER. YOU'VE BEEN CONDITIONED BY YEARS OF REJECTION AND GENERAL DISDAIN.

WE'RE LUCKY THAT WAY.

OVERALL, I RATED YOUR PERFORMANCE AS "SIMIAN."

THANKS!

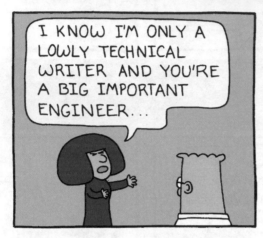

I HIRED A NEW DIRECTOR OF HUMAN RESOURCES TO HANDLE THE DOWN-SIZING.

I NEEDED SOMEBODY WHO ACTS LIKE A FRIEND BUT SECRETLY DELIGHTS IN THE MISERY OF ALL PEOPLE.

S. Adams
3-20

WE NEED TO TALK, PAUL. BUT FIRST I'M GOING TO BAT YOUR HEAD AROUND AND SCRATCH YOU.

HEE HEE!! THAT'S SO CUTE!

© 1995 United Feature Syndicate, Inc. (NYC)

CATBERT THE HR DIRECTOR

HERE'S THE NEW ORG CHART. MAYBE YOU'RE ON IT AND MAYBE NOT.

S. Adams

OOH! NICE TRY! SO CLOSE. TOO BAD.

3-21

© 1995 United Feature Syndicate, Inc. (NYC)

IT'S FUN TO PLAY WITH THEM BEFORE DOWNSIZING THEM.

COME SEE THE NEW ORG CHART.

S. Adams

OOPS, CHANGED MY MIND!

WHAM!!

3-22

© 1995 United Feature Syndicate, Inc. (NYC)

OUCHIE.

I'M SORE, BUT I'VE NEVER FELT SO FREE.

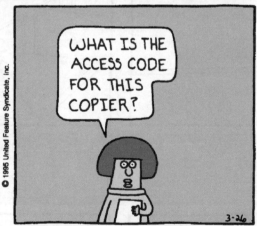

IN A WAY, I'M GLAD THE ELBONIANS RUN THIS COMPANY NOW.

AFTER YEARS OF BEING THE ONLY FEMALE ENGINEER I'LL ENJOY WATCHING THE ELBONIANS DISCRIMINATE AGAINST YOU GUYS.

CONTINUED...

I DIDN'T REALIZE YOU HAD COFFEE WENCHES IN THIS COUNTRY TOO.

I HOPE YOU DON'T WANT CHILDREN, YORGI.

I'D LIKE TO KICK-OFF THE PROJECT WITH THE TRADITIONAL BAD-MOUTHING OF THE GUY WHO WORKED ON THIS BEFORE.

HE'S SO SLIMY THAT SLUGS POUR SALT ON HIM. HIS BRAIN WOULD RATTLE IN A FLEA'S SKULL!

OH, AND I'LL NEED YOUR FILES.

FLEAS DON'T HAVE "SKULLS"!!

JUST AS I THOUGHT, MY CUBICLE IS TWO INCHES SMALLER TODAY THAN YESTERDAY!

WE INSTALLED REAL-TIME STATUS ADJUSTERS IN THE CUBICLE WALLS. SENSORS MONITOR YOUR WORK AND ADJUST THE CUBICLE SIZE ACCORDING TO YOUR VALUE.

IT'S AMAZING HOW FAST YOU GET USED TO IT.

THE **7** HABITS OF

HIGHLY DEFECTIVE PEOPLE

OW!

S. Adams

1. IGNORE ANY SIGNS OF DISCOMFORT IN OTHERS.

BUT HEY, I'VE BEEN DOING ALL OF THE TALKING.

2. USE HUMOR TO BELITTLE PEOPLE IN PUBLIC.

OUR NEWEST TEAM MEMBER HAS MOVIE STAR LOOKS. SPECIFICALLY, LASSIE.

3. TREAT ALL COMPLAINTS AS THE COMPLAINER'S FAULT.

YOU DON'T MOTIVATE ME.

MAYBE YOU SHOULD SEE A THERAPIST.

4. SHOW UP LATE AND RAISE CONTROVERSIAL ISSUES.

I THINK WE SHOULD LICENSE "BARNEY" AS OUR MASCOT.

© 1995 United Feature Syndicate, Inc.

5-7

5. GIVE ADVICE ON THINGS YOU DON'T UNDERSTAND.

TRY WRITING SOME ASSEMBLY LINE CODE HERE.

6. USE COMPLIMENTS TO SHOW YOUR PREJUDICES.

OOH, NICE CRISP PHOTO-COPY, ALICE. I DON'T THINK A MAN COULD HAVE DONE IT BETTER!

7. THINK THE COMICS ARE NOT ABOUT YOU

HEE HEE! LOOK AT THE HAIR ON THAT GUY!

95

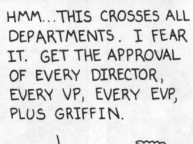

WHO NEEDS TO SIGN MY BUSINESS CASE TO BUY A WEB SERVER?

HMM...THIS CROSSES ALL DEPARTMENTS. I FEAR IT. GET THE APPROVAL OF EVERY DIRECTOR, EVERY VP, EVERY EVP, PLUS GRIFFIN.

DO YOU MEAN TED GRIFFIN IN FINANCE OR THE MYTHICAL GRIFFIN BEAST THAT'S HALF EAGLE, HALF LION?

WHICHEVER IS HARDER.

HA HA! NOW THAT THE ENGINEERS MUST CHARGE THEIR TIME TO MARKETING, WE OWN YOU!

I'LL JUST REPROGRAM YOUR COMPUTER THROUGH THE LAN SO ITS RADIATION WILL ALTER YOUR DNA.

IS THAT POSSIBLE??!

AS FAR AS YOU KNOW.

I TOLD A GUY IN MARKETING THAT I PROGRAMMED HIS COMPUTER TO ALTER HIS DNA STRUCTURE.

HEE HEE

HE THINKS HE'LL TURN INTO SOME KIND OF ANIMAL.

TELL HIM YOU SET IT TO "WEASEL." IT'LL TAKE LONGER TO NOTICE ANY CHANGE.

TELL ME THE TRUTH, ALICE. CAN DILBERT REPROGRAM MY DNA?

YEAH. YOU MARKETING GUYS ONLY HAVE ONE HELIX.

MAYBE YOU SHOULDN'T HAVE TOLD STAN YOU REPROGRAMMED HIS DNA THROUGH THE LAN.

THOSE MARKETING GUYS BELIEVE ANYTHING. THEY EVEN BELIEVE MARKET RESEARCH, FOR HEAVEN'S SAKE.

THERE'S NO TELLING WHAT THE POWER OF SUGGESTION MIGHT DO.

WELL, THANK YOU VERY MUCH.

7/5 © 1995 United Feature Syndicate, Inc. (NYC)

I JOKINGLY TOLD STAN IN MARKETING THAT I REPROGRAMMED HIS DNA. HE'S SO GULLIBLE THAT HE'S ACTUALLY CHANGING!

YOU MUST USE HIS GULLIBILITY TO REVERSE THE PROCESS. REMEMBER, HIS ENTIRE REALITY IS SHAPED BY UNVERIFIED CUSTOMER ANECDOTES.

I HEARD A RUMOR OF A STORY OF AN ALLEGED FOCUS GROUP WHERE A QUOTE TAKEN OUT OF CONTEXT INDICATES YOU'RE NOT BECOMING A WEASEL.

I'M NOT?!

YIPEEE!

7/6 © 1995 United Feature Syndicate, Inc. (NYC)

CAROL, THE NEXT TIME YOU ORDER MY BUSINESS CARDS, SPELL OUT MY FULL TITLE: "DIRECTOR OF PRODUCT ENHANCEMENTS."

DON'T USE THE ACRONYM "DOPE."

I DIDN'T KNOW YOU WERE THE DIRECTOR OF PRODUCT ENHANCEMENTS.

7/14 © 1995 United Feature Syndicate, Inc. (NYC)

Panel 1: I DON'T KNOW WHAT KIND OF GIFT TO BUY FOR TED'S BABY SHOWER.

Panel 2: HAND-CRAFTED ITEMS ARE GOOD. CUT THREE HOLES IN A PAPER BAG AND YOU'VE GOT A LOVELY BABY DRESS.

Panel 3: HE MIGHT THINK I'M CHEAP.

DO YOU THINK THE KID HAS A SALT SHAKER YET?

Panel 4: TED'S BABY SHOWER

OH LOOK, IT'S A STAPLER...

Panel 5: I CAN USE THIS TO TAKE UP THE HEM ON THE LOVELY HAND-CRAFTED PAPER BAG DRESS THAT DILBERT MADE.

Panel 6: IT LOOKS JUST LIKE THE ONE THAT DISAPPEARED FROM MY CUBICLE THIS MORNING.

EXCEPT YOURS HAD STAPLES.

Panel 7: CATBERT THE HR DIRECTOR

I THINK I'LL INVENT SOME ILLOGICAL POLICIES TO ANNOY EMPLOYEES.

Panel 8: MY DIABOLICAL NEW DRESS CODE WILL MAKE THEM QUESTION THEIR OWN SANITY.

Panel 9: ...SO, CASUAL CLOTHES DON'T LOWER OUR STOCK VALUE... BUT ONLY IF WORN ON FRIDAYS... UNLESS SOMEBODY SEES US... GOT IT?

I THINK I'M INSANE.

I DON'T UNDERSTAND YOUR NEW DRESS CODE POLICY, MR. CATBERT.

MAYBE YOU'RE INSANE.

IT'S SIMPLE. FRIDAYS ARE "CASUAL." BUT YOU CAN'T WEAR JEANS BECAUSE JEANS LOOK GOOD AND FEEL GOOD AND YOU ALREADY OWN SEVERAL PAIRS.

IT'S ANOTHER SADISTIC HUMAN RESOURCES PLOT TO MAKE PEOPLE QUIT!!

SAY HELLO TO UNSIGHTLY PANTY LINES.

MY STATUS FOR THE WEEK IS THAT THE ONGOING DEHUMANIZATION FROM MY JOB HAS CAUSED ME TO DOUBT MY EXISTENCE.

THERE IS REASON TO BELIEVE I AM BECOMING INVISIBLE.

DO I HEAR YOUR PAGER BUZZING, WALLY?

I DOUBT IT; I DON'T KEEP BATTERIES IN IT.

PLINK

THE DEHUMANIZATION OF MY JOB HAS RENDERED ME INVISIBLE TO HUMANS. ONLY YOU CAN SEE ME, DOGBERT.

HOW CAN WE FIX THIS?

YOU COULD WEAR A BAG ON YOUR HEAD WHEN YOU'RE AROUND ME.

THAT'S NOT THE FIX I HAD IN MIND.

IT'S NOT A PERFECT SOLUTION. I'D STILL BE ABLE TO HEAR YOU.

YOU'RE INVISIBLE TO YOUR CO-WORKERS. BUT YOU CAN COMPENSATE BY FORMING A SYMBIOTIC RELATIONSHIP WITH A VISIBLE CREATURE.

RATBERT WILL CLING TO YOUR BACK. HE'LL BE YOUR VISUAL AND AUDITORY LINK WITH YOUR CO-WORKERS.

SO... WORKING HARD? OR HARDLY WORKING?

I KNEW THIS COLOMBIAN COFFEE WAS TROUBLE.

DON'T BE ALARMED. I'M NOT REALLY A RAT FLOATING IN MIDAIR.

I'M CLINGING TO THE BACK OF AN EMPLOYEE WHO HAS BEEN RENDERED INVISIBLE BY A LONG SUCCESSION OF WORTHLESS ASSIGNMENTS.

LOOKS LIKE AN ISOLATED CASE OF BAD ATTITUDE.

WHICH ROOM IS THE "QUALITY" MEETING IN?

IF IT'S OKAY, I'LL HOLD ONTO MY SOUL WHILE I VISIT THE ACCOUNTING DEPARTMENT.

SOUL CHECK

I CAME TO ANSWER YOUR QUESTIONS ABOUT MY EXPENSE REPORT.

TAKE A SEAT.

I DON'T LIKE THE WAY THIS IS STARTING.

DILBERT'S EXPENSE VOUCHER

WHAT ARE YOU TRYING TO PULL?? DO YOU THINK WE'RE IDIOTS IN ACCOUNTING?!!

NO, I SWEAR, I THINK YOU'RE SMART BUT SADISTIC TROLLS WITH MANY HUMANOID CHARACTERISTICS.

APPARENTLY THERE WAS NO RIGHT ANSWER.

DILBERT'S EXPENSE VOUCHER

YOU SPENT NEARLY $10 PER DAY ON MEALS DURING YOUR TRIP.

THE TRAVEL GUIDELINES REQUIRE YOU TO STUN A PIGEON WITH YOUR BRIEFCASE ON THE WAY TO THE HOTEL THEN FRY IT UP ON YOUR TRAVEL IRON.

I TRIED... BUT IT WAS TAKING SO LONG.

TRY THE "WOOL" SETTING.

DILBERT IS TRAPPED IN THE BOWELS OF ACCOUNTING

I UNDERSTAND YOU HAVE DILBERT IN THERE. FREE HIM, OR ELSE...

ELSE WHAT?

OR ELSE I WILL PUT THIS CAP ON MY HEAD BACKWARDS! YOUR LITTLE HARDWIRED ACCOUNTING BRAIN WILL EXPLODE JUST LOOKING AT IT.

WHAT WAS THAT POPPING SOUND?

A PARADIGM SHIFTING WITHOUT A CLUTCH.

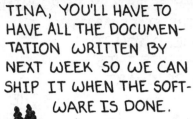
TINA, YOU'LL HAVE TO HAVE ALL THE DOCUMENTATION WRITTEN BY NEXT WEEK SO WE CAN SHIP IT WHEN THE SOFTWARE IS DONE.

HOW CAN I WRITE INSTRUCTIONS FOR SOMETHING THAT DOESN'T EXIST YET?

YOU'LL HAVE TO MAKE LOGICAL GUESSES.

"IF YOU PRESS ANY KEY YOUR COMPUTER WILL LOCK UP. IF YOU CALL OUR TECH SUPPORT WE'LL BLAME 'MICROSOFT.'"

I FEEL LIKE TWEAKING SOME BRITTLE PEOPLE. DO YOU KNOW ANY BRITTLE PEOPLE?

TRY TINA THE TECH WRITER. SHE BELIEVES THAT ALL FORMS OF EXPRESSION ARE AN INSULT TO HER GENDER AND HER PROFESSION.

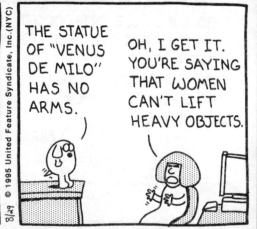
THE STATUE OF "VENUS DE MILO" HAS NO ARMS.

OH, I GET IT. YOU'RE SAYING THAT WOMEN CAN'T LIFT HEAVY OBJECTS.

DOGBERT TWEAKS TINA THE BRITTLE TECH WRITER.

WHAT DO YOU THINK OF THE MOVIE "THELMA AND LOUISE"?

I KNOW WHAT YOU'RE TRYING TO SAY. YOU THINK ALL WOMEN ARE BAD DRIVERS. THAT'S REALLY THE POINT OF THE MOVIE, ISN'T IT??

IF YOU'RE NOT OFFENDED YET, TUNE IN TOMORROW.

THE "THREE STOOGES"?

WHY ARE ALL OF THE DOCUMENTARIES ABOUT MEN??!

DOGBERT TWEAKS TINA THE BRITTLE TECH WRITER

IS TECHNICAL WRITING THE SAME AS WORD PROCESSING?

NO!!!

I AM A HIGHLY SKILLED COMMUNICATIONS PROFESSIONAL! I CAN TAKE JUMBLES OF INERT THOUGHTS AND BRING THEM TO LIFE!!

MY SECRETARY IS RUNNING THE STAFF MEETING. I NEED YOU TO RETYPE THIS ORG CHART.

THE DOCTOR IS IN!

THIS WEEK WE INTRODUCED TINA THE BRITTLE TECH WRITER TO THE STRIP. TINA IS DYSFUNCTIONAL LIKE EVERYBODY HERE EXCEPT ME.

RRRR

SEND YOUR OPINIONS BY E-MAIL TO SCOTTADAMS@AOL.COM

IT'S THE ONLY WAY WE CAN LEARN.

RRRR

PICK ONE

A. WOMEN SHOULD ONLY BE PORTRAYED AS LAWYERS AND STARSHIP CAPTAINS.

B. I DON'T HAVE E-MAIL.

C. TINA SHOULD BE TREATED WITH THE SAME DIGNITY AS DILBERT AND WALLY.

D. TAKE AN ART CLASS.

PROFITS ARE DOWN, MORALE IS SINKING; IT'S TIME FOR BOLD LEADERSHIP!!

SO I GOT SOME INSPIRATIONAL POSTERS FEATURING A VARIETY OF RELEVANT NATURE SCENES.

I THINK YOU CAN RELATE TO THIS SCENE.

AM I THE SEAGULL OR THE CLAM?

MY NEW INSPIRATIONAL POSTER IS SO EFFECTIVE THAT I DECIDED TO CARRY IT WITH ME.

WHAT DO YOU THINK, ALICE? ARE YOU INSPIRED?

I'D REALLY HAVE TO SEE THE FRONT...

HMM... I DON'T THINK THERE'S A WIN-WIN SCENARIO HERE...

TELL ME ABOUT IT...

HERE'S MY TIME SHEET, FILLED OUT IN INCREMENTS OF FIFTEEN MINUTES.

AS USUAL, I CODED THE USELESS HOURS SPENT IN MEETINGS AS "WORK," WHEREAS THE TIME I SPENT IN THE SHOWER DESIGNING CIRCUITS IN MY MIND IS "NON-WORK."

INTERESTINGLY, EVEN THE TIME I SPEND COMPLAINING ABOUT MY LACK OF PRODUCTIVITY IS CONSIDERED "WORK."

I HATE MY LIFE.

ALICE IS SITTING IN FOR THE BOSS!

PRODUCTIVITY AT LAST !!!

EFFICIENCY! YES!!

AS LONG AS SHE DOESN'T GET AN ATTITUDE...

ALICE SITS IN FOR THE BOSS

I WILL APPROVE YOUR EXPENSE VOUCHER ON ONE CONDITION.

YOU MUST SLAY THE CREATURE WHO STALKS THE OFFICE AT NIGHT AND EATS OUR HIDDEN SNACKS!!!

IT HAS TO BE EITHER YOU OR THE SECURITY GUARD.

SLAY HIM FIRST AND SEE IF THE PROBLEM STOPS.

WE'RE POISED FOR SUCCESS. WE EXPECT HUGE EARNINGS AND INCREASED MARKET SHARE!

NEXT ON THE AGENDA... THERE WILL BE NO RAISES BECAUSE IT WILL BE A DIFFICULT YEAR...

CAROL, I THOUGHT I TOLD YOU TO PUT THE "UNITED WAY" UPDATE BETWEEN THOSE TWO AGENDA ITEMS.

OOPSIE.

CATBERT THE H.R. DIRECTOR

MY JOB IS TOO STRESSFUL. CAN I SEE A COMPANY COUNSELOR?

I RE-ENGINEERED OUR COUNSELING PROCESS. NOW WE PUT YOU IN A BIG HOLE AND COVER YOU WITH SAND.

IF THIS IS MY ONLY BENEFIT I'D BETTER GET A LOT OF SAND!

JUST KEEP YOUR MOUTH OPEN.

CAROL, ABOUT THIS FLIGHT TO NEW YORK THAT YOU BOOKED FOR ME...

IS IT REALLY NECESSARY TO MAKE ALL THESE STOPOVERS IN THIRD-WORLD COUNTRIES THAT ARE EXPERIENCING REBEL INSURRECTIONS?

YOU'D BETTER WEAR THE INTERNATIONAL SYMBOL OF THE "RED CROSS" ON YOUR BACK.

TERRIBLE NEWS: MY BOSS ASSIGNED ME TO A FUN AND VALUABLE PROJECT.

UH-OH. THAT MEANS AT LEAST THREE MORONS WILL BE ASSIGNED TO SIMILAR PROJECTS. YOU MUST FIND THEM AND CRUSH THEM...

EXACTLY.

CARL, OLD BUDDY, WHATCHA WORKIN' ON THESE DAYS?

NOTHING FUN AND VALUABLE. SHOO SHOO!!

IT LOOKS LIKE SOMEBODY IS USING BINDERS TO ILLEGALLY INCREASE THE SIZE OF HIS CUBICLE.

YOU THINK YOUR STATUS WILL INCREASE WITH YOUR CUBICLE SIZE, DON'T YOU! WELL, IT WON'T WORK!

HERE'S A RAISE. I DON'T KNOW WHY.

PSSST. IS HE SEEING ANYBODY?

RRRR

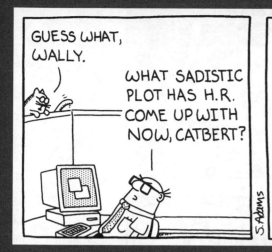

GUESS WHAT, WALLY.

WHAT SADISTIC PLOT HAS H.R. COME UP WITH NOW, CATBERT?

WE'RE GIVING YOU A REAL BOSS PLUS A "DOTTED LINE" TO ANOTHER BOSS WHO HAS DIFFERENT OBJECTIVES.

THE STATUS REPORTS ALONE WILL TAKE FORTY HOURS A WEEK.

I'M GONNA STAPLE MYSELF TO DEATH.

A WHILE BACK I ASKED FOR OPINIONS ABOUT THIS NEW CHARACTER, "TINA THE BRITTLE TECH WRITER."

RRRR

RESULTS

MOST PEOPLE, INCLUDING NEARLY ALL SELF-DESCRIBED FEMINISTS, SAID KEEP HER. BUT THERE WERE MANY REQUESTS TO ADD "NON-STEREOTYPICAL" FEMALE CHARACTERS FOR BALANCE.

IN THE INTEREST OF BALANCE I GIVE YOU "ANTINA."

IS ANYBODY UP FOR SOME MATH?

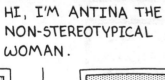

HI, I'M ANTINA THE NON-STEREOTYPICAL WOMAN.

THAT COMPUTER MONITOR YOU'RE USING IS SUPPOSED TO BE 17 INCHES. BUT IT'S MORE LIKE 16.5 INCHES.

I TOOK THE COFFEE MACHINE APART JUST FOR FUN — WANT TO SEE?

I'VE DECIDED TO MASK MY BOYISH LOOKS BY GROWING A BEARD.

I DIDN'T THINK TED WAS SMART ENOUGH TO KNOW HOW TO GROW A BEARD.

HEE HEE

TWO WEEKS LATER

HOW DO YOU LIKE MY BEARD?

MY SEARCH FOR A NEW MANAGER IS OVER.

I PROMOTED TED TO BE YOUR NEW MANAGER. I USED TO THINK HE LOOKED BOYISH, BUT HIS NEW BEARD CHANGED THAT.

ARE EITHER OF YOU THE LEAST BIT CONCERNED THAT TED'S BEARD IS GROWING FROM HIS FOREHEAD?

SHE MADE IT SOUND AS IF IT'S WRONG.

YOU CAN PUNISH THEM FOR HAVING BAD OPINIONS.

AS YOUR NEW BOSS I HAVE YET TO SELECT MY "PET" EMPLOYEE. I SHALL DO THIS BY CLOSING MY EYES AND POINTING THE BEARD ON MY FOREHEAD.

TO MAKE IT FAIR, I'LL CLOSE MY EYES WHILE ONE OF YOU SPINS MY CHAIR!

STAIRS

ALICE... UM... TECHNICALLY THIS ISN'T "SPINNING."

ASOK THE INTERN

ASOK, COME QUICKLY! IT'S AN EMERGENCY!

YOU MUST CRAWL THROUGH THE JEFFRIES TUBE AND SHUT DOWN THE FURNACE BEFORE IT FRIES US ALL!

TODAY YOUNG ASOK LEARNS THAT LIFE IS NOT LIKE "STAR TREK."

I'M STUCK.

SPANK THE INTERN 50¢

I WANT EVERYONE TO PREPARE A PRESENTATION FOR THE EXECUTIVE REVIEW BOARD. URGENT.

WHAT'S THAT SMELL? YES!!! ... IT'S THE SCENT OF UNNECESSARY WORK FOR A MEETING THAT WILL BE CANCELED.

SNIFF SNIFF

DID YOU SMELL THE UNNECESSARY WORK? WE CAN IGNORE IT!

IT'S LIKE POPCORN FOR THE SOUL.

URGENT

WHY AREN'T YOU SLAVING AWAY, PREPARING FOR THE EXECUTIVE REVIEW BOARD MEETING?

I HAVE THE MALE "WORK AVOIDANCE CHROMOSOME." I CAN DETECT UNNECESSARY WORK, THEREBY AVOIDING IT.

WE ALL HAVE TO BE READY TO PRESENT SOMETHING!

COULD YOU HOLD IT DOWN? I'M TRYING TO SLEEP.

IT'S MY HONOR TO PRESENT THIS SPECIAL BONUS CHECK TO BARRY.

THAT'S YOU.

MY NAME IS BARRY??

THIS IS FOR WORKING HUNDREDS OF HOURS OF OVERTIME.

WHILE YOU QUITTERS WERE GOING HOME BY 9 PM EVERY NIGHT...

BARRY REMAINED AT WORK STARING AT HIS COMPUTER FOR HOURS.

IT'S IMPORTANT TO RECOGNIZE EXTRA EFFORT.

SADLY, THAT'S THE END OF THE SPECIAL BONUS BUDGET FOR THE YEAR.

BURP

IN RETROSPECT, I SHOULDN'T HAVE TOLD BARRY THAT HIS SCREEN SAVER IS AN EPIC MINI-SERIES.

I DON'T BELIEVE MEN HAVE A SPECIAL CHROMOSOME TO TELL THEM WHICH ASSIGNMENTS ARE A WASTE OF TIME.

WE DO.

I WILL TEST THE THEORY ON YOUNG ASOK THE INTERN.

MMM... THE SWEET SMELL OF UNNECESSARY WORK.

MAYBE MEN ARE MORE PERCEPTIVE THAN YOU'D THINK.

SHE'S AROUSED. I'LL MAKE MY MOVE.

I WANT YOU THREE TO WRITE THE DEPARTMENT NEWSLETTER. IT'S AN IMPORTANT, HIGH-PROFILE ASSIGNMENT.

I AM AN EXPERIENCED TECHNICAL WRITER. YOU HAVE PLACED ME ON A PROJECT WITH AN INTERN AND A RODENT.

MY NEXT RAISE WILL DEPEND ON THEIR PERFORMANCE.

I'LL DO THE SPORTS PAGE!

I'LL BE THE TOPLESS MODEL ON PAGE TWO.

LET'S GET ONE THING STRAIGHT BEFORE WE START WRITING THE DEPARTMENT NEWSLETTER...

I'M AN EXPERIENCED TECHNICAL WRITER. YOU ARE AN INTERN AND A RAT, RESPECTIVELY. THEREFORE I WILL BE THE EDITOR.

I HAVE NO SKILLS WHATSOEVER. THEREFORE I'LL BE EXECUTIVE EDITOR.

IS "PUBLISHER" TAKEN?

WALLY, I'M HOPING YOU'LL AGREE TO WRITE ABOUT YOUR PROJECT FOR THE NEWSLETTER...

AND IN THE GRAND TRADITION OF ENGINEERING, I EXPECT YOU'LL GIVE THIS THE LOWEST PRIORITY, THUS MAKING ME DESPISE YOU.

SO... ARE YOU SAYING YOU DON'T DESPISE ME NOW?

WE ARE NOT HAVING A "MOMENT" HERE!

PERFORMANCE REVIEW

YOUR MAIN ACCOMPLISHMENT WAS THE DEPARTMENT NEWSLETTER WHICH WAS BOTH UNINTERESTING AND UNIMPORTANT. YOU GET NO RAISE.

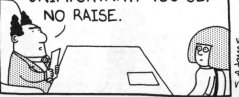

THE NEWSLETTER WAS YOUR IDEA, AND IT'S BORING BECAUSE MOST OF THE ARTICLES ARE CONTRIBUTED BY MY IDIOTIC COWORKERS.

YOU DON'T SEEM TO UNDERSTAND THE VALUE OF TEAMWORK.

I UNDERSTAND ITS VALUE; IT JUST COST ME A TWO-PERCENT RAISE.

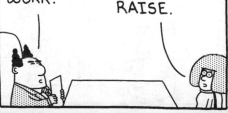

THE EXECUTIVE REVIEW BOARD MEETING IS CANCELED. I HOPE YOU DIDN'T WORK TOO HARD PREPARING FOR IT.

MUST... CONTROL FIST... OF... DEATH...

UNLIKE ALICE, I SAW IT COMING AND DID NO WORK WHATSOEVER.

DID YOU SEE THAT COMING, NOSTRADAMUS?

OW

WHAT DOES THIS DO TO HEADCOUNT?

119

IT HAS COME TO MY ATTENTION THAT 40% OF YOUR SICK DAYS ARE ON FRIDAYS AND MONDAYS. THIS IS UNACCEPTABLE.

HA HA HA !!! THAT'S A GOOD ONE !!!

PLEASE TELL ME HE WAS KIDDING.

WELCOME TO HELL, KID.

I JUST WATCHED THE MANDATORY VIDEO ON SEXUAL HARASSMENT. IT WORKED!

IN ONLY THIRTY MINUTES, THAT VIDEO CORRECTED A BILLION YEARS OF EVOLUTION. DO SOMETHING SEXY AND WATCH ME IGNORE IT!

I PROBABLY SHOULDN'T HAVE FAST-FORWARDED THROUGH THE BORING PARTS.

HE SLIPS IN LIKE A PANTHER TO TAKE THE LAST CUP OF COFFEE AND NOT MAKE MORE.

I AM PHIL, THE PRINCE OF INSUFFICIENT LIGHT! I DARN YOU TO HECK !!!

PHIL?

YOU WERE ALWAYS MOM'S GOLDEN BOY.

SOMEBODY BROUGHT POTATO SALAD. GIVE ME YOUR SPOON.

MOM WANTED ME TO BE A MANAGER LIKE YOU. BUT I CHOSE MY OWN PATH.

I BECAME PHIL, THE RULER OF HECK, THE PUNISHER OF MINOR SINS!

HOW DO YOU MAKE MONEY?

CORPORATE SPONSORSHIP. "PROCTER AND GAMBLE" PAYS ME TO STAY AWAY FROM THEM.

YOU SHOULD SELL A LINE OF HOME-EXERCISE SPOONS.

THIS IS PHIL, RULER OF HECK, WITH A SPECIAL OFFER FOR MY PATENTED "EXERSPOON."

YOU CAN DO OVER SEVEN MILLION EXERCISES WITH THE "EXERSPOON!" IT EVEN TRIMS PROBLEM AREAS!

AND THANKS TO THE INNOVATIVE SPOON SHAPE, STORAGE IS A BREEZE!

MMM...

I NEED THIS INFORMATION TODAY. PLUS A COMPLETE ANALYSIS OF THE ALTERNATIVES.

CRINKLE CRINKLE STUFF

THAT WASN'T NICE.

IN TODAY'S LESSON, YOU LEARN THAT YOU'RE MY CO-WORKER, NOT MY BOSS.

WALLY, I NEED YOUR INPUT ON THIS BY THE END OF THE DAY.

PLEASE DROP YOUR REQUEST HERE, IN "WALLY'S PILE OF PERPETUAL IGNORAGE."

CAN'T I JUST GIVE IT TO YOU?

I DON'T LIKE TO TOUCH THAT STUFF WITH MY HANDS.

CATBERT: EVIL HR DIRECTOR

HEY, WALLY... BIG LAYOFFS COMING.

I'VE SEEN THE LIST. I KNOW MORE ABOUT YOUR FUTURE THAN YOU DO. BUT IT'S A SECRET.

SADLY, CATS DON'T KEEP SECRETS VERY WELL.

NICE CHAIR.

I HEAR YOU'RE ON THE LAYOFF LIST, WALLY. HAS ANYONE CLAIMED YOUR CHAIR, YET?

I CLAIMED IT A FEW MINUTES AGO.

LIAR!

I GUESS IT'S TRUE WHAT THEY SAY ABOUT LAYOFFS BEING HARD ON THE SURVIVORS.

OW!

POW!!

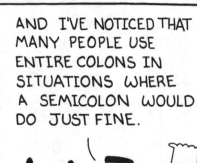

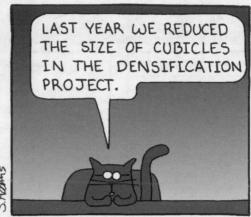

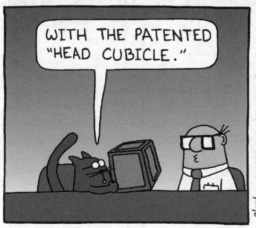

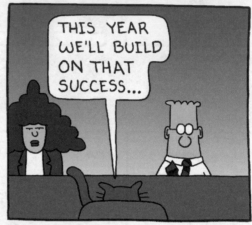

126

127

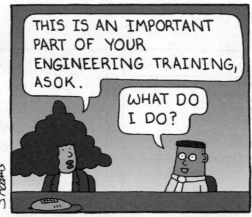

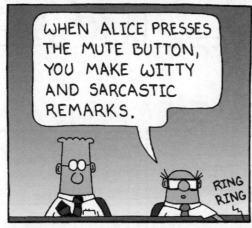

CATBERT: EVIL H.R. DIRECTOR

TO: ALL EMPLOYEES
THE SMELL OF POPCORN IN THE OFFICE IS UNPROFESSIONAL...

HE'S BANNING POPCORN! FIRST IT WAS TOBACCO, THEN PERFUME, NOW THIS... THERE'S ONLY ONE POLLUTANT LEFT.

...THIS BRINGS ME TO THE UNPLEASANT SUBJECT OF WALLY...

I'VE DECIDED TO END MY LONELINESS BY GETTING A MAIL-ORDER BRIDE FROM ELBONIA.

THE PHOTOS WERE GRAINY, BUT THE ADVERTISEMENT GUARANTEES THAT SHE'S CUTE.

ELBONIA

BLONDE.

wigs

MY ELBONIAN MAIL-ORDER BRIDE WILL ARRIVE ANY DAY NOW.

WHY DON'T YOU KNOW THE EXACT DATE?

BECAUSE THEY'RE SENDING HER BY MAIL. I WASN'T WILLING TO PAY FOR OVERNIGHT DELIVERY.

SHE'S ONE LUCKY GAL.

I'LL PROBABLY KEEP HER IN THE GARAGE. IT HAS A SINK.

131

CAROL, COULD YOU CHECK OUR POINTY-HAIRED BOSS'S CALENDAR?

GRUMBLE

WE'D LIKE TO SCHEDULE A CELEBRATION FOR THE ENGINEERS WHO GOT PATENTS.

GRUMBLE

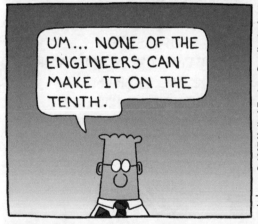

WE'RE ALL AVAILABLE ON THE SIXTH, NINTH, TWENTIETH AND THE TWENTY-FIRST.

I'LL SCHEDULE IT FOR THE TENTH. THAT'S THE ONLY DAY HE CAN DO IT.

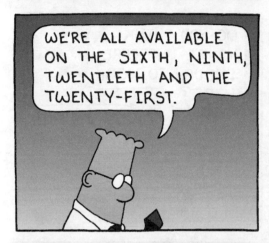

UM... NONE OF THE ENGINEERS CAN MAKE IT ON THE TENTH.

IT'S NOT A PERFECT WORLD.

WHEN'S THE PATENT CELEBRATION?

SHUT UP

ON THE TENTH

WE SHOULD DO THIS MORE OFTEN.

YEAH, I LIKE CAKE.

JOB INTERVIEW

WE'RE LOOKING FOR A SPECIAL KIND OF EMPLOYEE, WALLY.

SPECIFICALLY, WE LIKE PEOPLE WITH LOW SELF-ESTEEM.

THAT WAY WE CAN BULLY THEM INTO WORKING UNPAID OVERTIME.

DO YOU THINK YOU'RE INSECURE ENOUGH TO WORK HERE?

LET ME PUT IT THIS WAY.

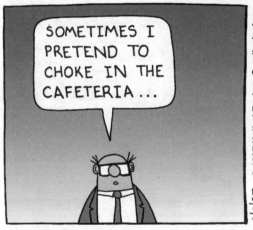

SOMETIMES I PRETEND TO CHOKE IN THE CAFETERIA...

THEN WHEN SOMEONE PERFORMS THE HEIMLICH MANEUVER ON ME I SPIN AROUND SUDDENLY...

JUST TO GET A HUG.

DID HE REALLY SAY YOU'RE OVER-QUALIFIED?

AAK! MMPH!

2/9/97 © 1997 United Feature Syndicate, Inc.

134

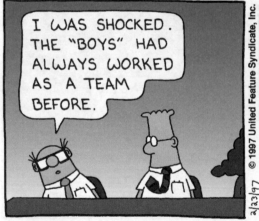

HERE'S MY PROJECT PLAN AS YOU REQUESTED.

OUR TEAM IS ALREADY WORKING DAY AND NIGHT ON OTHER PROJECTS.

I ASSUMED WE'D GIVE UP EATING, SLEEPING AND BATHING TO FIT THIS IN.

BY THE SECOND WEEK WE'LL BE STARVING, DELIRIOUS AND STINKING.

WE'LL BE LIKE WILD, UNPREDICTABLE ANIMALS.

SPECIFICALLY, WE'D BE LIKE WILD CHIPMUNKS. NONE OF US ARE VERY AGGRESSIVE.

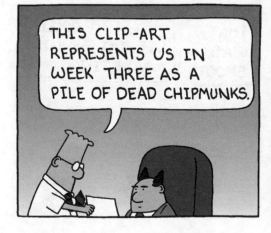

THIS CLIP-ART REPRESENTS US IN WEEK THREE AS A PILE OF DEAD CHIPMUNKS.

NOW HE WANTS IT IN TWO WEEKS?

NEVER MIX SARCASM WITH GOOD CLIP-ART.

138

HEY, WALLY. I HEAR YOU'RE GETTING AN ELBONIAN MAIL-ORDER BRIDE!

IT'S SO SAD AND PATHETIC, YET SO FUNNY! I FEEL SORRY FOR HER ALREADY!

HU-HAHAHA HA HA HA HA HA

AND PEOPLE ASK WHY I GAVE UP ON LOCAL GIRLS.

I HATE TO INTERRUPT YOUR LOUD CONVERSATION OUTSIDE MY CUBICLE...

BUT IF YOU DON'T GO AWAY, I'LL POUND YOUR INCONSIDERATE HEAD SO FAR INTO YOUR TORSO THAT YOU HAVE TO DROP YOUR PANTS TO SAY HELLO.

DID YOU JUST HEAR A STRANGE NOISE?

IT SOUNDED LIKE, "MELP! MELP!"

DILBERT, YOU'LL WORK WITH "KENNY THE SALES-WEASEL" ON OUR BIGGEST PROSPECT.

TELL ME ALL OF OUR PRODUCT'S TECHNICAL SPECS ON THE WAY. I LIKE TO BE PREPARED.

OUR PRODUCT IS BEIGE. IT USES ELECTRICITY.

WHOA! BRAIN OVERLOAD!

VISITING THE CUSTOMER

WHEN I INTRODUCE YOU TO THE CUSTOMER, SMILE AND GIVE HIM A HEARTY SLAP ON THE BACK.

GET READY. HERE HE COMES.

I'D BETTER TAKE SOME PRACTICE SWINGS.

NEXT TIME, LESS FOLLOW-THROUGH, AIM HIGHER, AND IF HE TURNS AROUND SUDDENLY, HOLD OFF.

SORRY

OW OW OW OW OW

VISITING THE CUSTOMER

I BROUGHT DILBERT TO EXPLAIN WHAT MAKES OUR PRODUCT SPECIAL.

IT'S EXACTLY LIKE OUR COMPETITOR'S PRODUCT EXCEPT WE CHARGE MORE TO COVER THE COST OF OUR DECEPTIVE ADVERTISING.

WHILE YOU'RE UP, COULD YOU GET ME A CUP OF COFFEE?

VISITING THE CUSTOMER

NO ONE HAS EVER BEEN FIRED FOR BUYING OUR PRODUCT!

THAT'S TRUE.

THERE IS THE OCCASIONAL SAVAGE BEATING... AND MORE THAN OUR SHARE OF SUICIDES...

BUT THAT HAS "STATISTICAL CLUSTERING" WRITTEN ALL OVER IT.

ASOK THE INTERN EXPLAINS THE NEW RULES OF BODY LANGUAGE

FAKE HAPPINESS

THIS MEANS: I AM NOT MOTIVATED BY THE SIZE OF MY PAYCHECK.

AHH!! WAHH! WAHH!

THIS MEANS: I AM SLIGHTLY CONCERNED ABOUT THE IMPENDING REORGANIZATION.

THIS MEANS: I HAVE DECIDED TO WORK IN THE MARKETING FIELD.

COUNTER-CLOCKWISE SPIN

THIS MEANS: I AM BEING SARCASTIC.

OH, THERE'S A GOOD PLAN.

NOTE LIPS →

THIS MEANS: THE RECENT EMPLOYEE SATISFACTION SURVEY HAS NOT CAPTURED THE EXTENT OF MY FEELINGS.

THIS MEANS: I THINK YOU ARE ATTRACTIVE BUT IT WOULD BE VERY UNPROFESSIONAL TO SHOW IT.

THIS MEANS: MY LOTTERY INVESTMENT PAID OFF.

YANK!

144

WHAT IF...

ALBERT EINSTEIN HAD BEEN IN MARKETING?

I HAVE A GREAT IDEA FOR INCREASING SALES.

NOPE. THIS WILL NEVER WORK.

UM... IS IT POSSIBLE THAT YOU DON'T FULLY UNDERSTAND THE IDEA?

THAT'S QUITE AN EGO YOU HAVE THERE, ALLAN.

ALBERT.

EXPERIENCED MANAGERS KNOW HOW TO IDENTIFY BAD IDEAS...

BAD IDEAS COME FROM OTHER PEOPLE.

NOW GO WORK SMARTER, NOT HARDER.

I WORRY THAT A GUY LIKE THAT WILL GO OFF AND BUILD A HUGE BOMB.

Panel 1: I ADMIRE YOUR WORK ETHIC, ALICE. YOU'RE EVEN WORKING DURING YOUR VACATION.

Panel 2: IT MUST BE HARD TO REMAIN MOTIVATED WHEN YOU KNOW YOU CAN NEVER BREAK THROUGH THE GLASS CEILING.

Panel 3: SO, IT LOOKS LIKE IT'S JUST TILE AFTER ALL.

Panel 1: I AM MORDAC THE REFUSER. I AM HERE TO DISCUSS YOUR REQUEST FOR A COMPUTER UPGRADE.

Panel 2: CRINKLE! MMPHH! CHOMP CHOMP CHOMP

Panel 3: WE LOTHT THUH PAHPER-WUHK. THAT'S A HUGE SURPRISE. LUCKILY I MADE SEVENTY-FIVE EXTRA COPIES.

Panel 1: I AM MORDAC THE PREVENTER, YOUR LIASON FROM THE INFORMATION TECHNOLOGY DEPARTMENT.

Panel 2: I COME WITH TALES OF RESOURCE SHORTAGES. YOUR REQUEST FOR OUR SERVICES IS DENIED.

Panel 3: I DIDN'T REQUEST ANY OF YOUR SERVICES. DON'T TRY YOUR REVERSE PSYCHOLOGY ON ME.

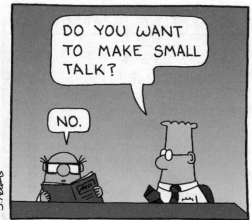

149

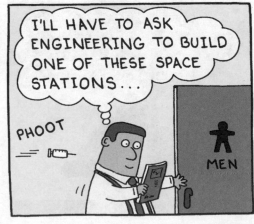

150

WHEN YOU SHOW THIS TO OUR VP, PUT IN SOME REVENUE FIGURES.

THERE'S NO REVENUE. ALL WE'RE DOING IS UPGRADING OUR NETWORK.

S. Adams

I MIGHT HAVE TOLD HIM THE PROJECT HAS REVENUES.

LET'S NOT CONFUSE HIM BY CHANGING THE STORY NOW.

YI-YI-YI

O-O-O-OKAY. HOW MUCH REVENUE DO YOU WANT? A MILLION DOLLARS?

11/23/97 © 1997 United Feature Syndicate, Inc.

I MIGHT HAVE TOLD HIM IT WAS MORE.

JUST TELL ME WHAT LIE TO USE !!!

CAN'T YOU CALCULATE IT ON THE SPREAD-SHEET?

MUST... CONTROL... FIST...OF... DEATH...

151

WE DON'T HAVE A CUBICLE AVAILABLE FOR YOU YET, BRUCE.

SO I'M DECLARING THIS PART OF THE CARPET TO BE YOUR OFFICE.

IF SOMEONE GOES TO A MEETING, YOU CAN SNEAK INTO HIS CUBICLE AND USE THE PHONE.

OUR COMPUTER BUDGET IS GONE, BUT WE HAVE AN OLD MONITOR THAT YOU CAN PUT ON TOP OF YOUR BRIEFCASE.

CAN I PUT TAPE ON THE CARPET TO MARK MY BOUNDARY?

THAT WON'T BE NECESSARY, THANKS TO THIS HI-TECH DEVICE.

A DOG COLLAR?

IT WILL GIVE A MILD SHOCK IF YOU CROSS YOUR INVISIBLE BOUNDARY.

THE NEW GUY HASN'T LEFT THAT SPOT FOR A WEEK.

WALLY TAUGHT HIM TO BEG FOR FOOD.

Panel 1: HI. I'M DAN, THE ILLOGICAL SCIENTIST. THAT SOFTWARE YOU'RE WRITING WILL NEVER WORK, AND I CAN PROVE IT.

Panel 2: I DON'T MEAN TO BE RUDE, BUT IT'S NOT LOGICALLY POSSIBLE TO PROVE SOMETHING <u>CAN'T</u> BE DONE.

Panel 3: IT'S IMPOSSIBLE FOR MOST PEOPLE, BUT <u>I'M</u> A TRAINED SCIENTIST.

DID THE TRAINING INVOLVE ELECTRIC SHOCKS?

Panel 4: LET'S SEE... IT LOOKS LIKE YOU HAVEN'T SIGNED TED'S CARD YET.

Panel 5: STAMP

Panel 6: DO YOU THINK "CONGRATULATIONS" IS APPROPRIATE FOR A DEATH IN HIS FAMILY?

YOU NEVER KNOW.

Panel 7: ARE YOU FREE ON THURSDAY FOR TED'S SURPRISE PARTY?

Panel 8: PARTY? YOU DON'T GIVE A PARTY FOR SOMEONE WHO HAS A DEATH IN THE FAMILY.

WELL... WE GOT HIM A CARD, THEN FLOWERS. IT JUST SNOWBALLED.

Panel 9: I ASSUME THIS WILL ALL BE IN GOOD TASTE.

I CAN'T PROMISE THAT. KARAOKE IS REALLY HIT OR MISS.

TED'S BROTHER WAS A MOBSTER. LAST WEEK HE WAS KILLED BY A RIVAL FAMILY'S HIT TEAM.

WE GOT TED A SYMPATHY CARD, THEN IT SNOWBALLED INTO A SURPRISE PARTY FOR TOMORROW.

MY JOB IS TO WRITE A FUNNY SONG.

FOR HE'S A BURIED GOOD FELLOW... FOR HE'S A BURIED GOOD FELLOW... WHICH NOBODY CAN DENY.

GOOD

OUR NEW E-MAIL MONITORING SYSTEM SHOWS THAT YOU SENT A PERSONAL MESSAGE LAST WEEK.

COINCIDENTALLY, THE NEW ALICE MONITORING SYSTEM DETECTS TWENTY HOURS OF UNPAID OVERTIME.

ACCORDING TO THE MANUAL, PRODUCTIVITY WILL SOAR NOW.

BEEP... BEEP... BOOP... NOW DETECTING CLUELESSNESS IN THE VICINITY.

I'M OFF TO ELBONIA, THE LAND OF WAIST-DEEP MUD AND MISOGYNY.

ON THE PLUS SIDE, YOU CAN KICK PEOPLE AND BLAME IT ON THE MUD WEASELS.

WHAT'S WRONG, YUGI? ONE SECOND YOU ARE COMPLIMENTING THIS CHICK, NEXT SECOND SCREAMING.

MUD WEASEL.

Panel 1: I JUST READ THAT THE AVERAGE WOMAN IS PAID 75 CENTS FOR EVERY DOLLAR THAT MEN MAKE. IT'S AN OUTRAGE!

Panel 2: I'M THE HIGHEST PAID ENGINEER IN THE COMPANY.

Panel 3: THAT'S IMPOSSIBLE. THE ARTICLE SAYS "AVERAGE WOMEN" EARN LESS.

SUDDENLY, THE PROBLEM COMES INTO FOCUS.

3/16/98 © 1998 United Feature Syndicate, Inc.

Panel 1: THIS ARTICLE SAYS MEN ARE PAID 25% MORE THAN WOMEN. HOW DO YOU EXPLAIN THAT?

Panel 2: ACTUALLY, IT SAYS WOMEN MAKE 75¢ FOR EVERY DOLLAR THAT MEN MAKE. THAT'S <u>33%</u> MORE FOR MEN.

ESTRO

Panel 3: I SUPPOSE THERE'S ALMOST NO CHANCE YOU'LL PRAISE ME FOR MY MATH SKILLS RIGHT NOW.

3/17/98 © 1998 United Feature Syndicate, Inc.

Panel 1: ALICE, ONE DAY I HOPE WE CAN BE JUDGED BY OUR ACCOMPLISHMENTS AND NOT OUR GENDER.

Panel 2: I GOT MY FOURTEENTH PATENT TODAY. I'M ON MY WAY TO A LUNCH BANQUET IN MY HONOR.

Panel 3: AND YOU WORE <u>THAT</u>?

3/18/98 © 1998 United Feature Syndicate, Inc.

YOUR CUBICLE HAS BEEN REPLACED BY A "PERSONAL HABITAT."

IT'S EXACTLY LIKE YOUR CUBICLE BUT MUCH LESS CLUTTERED.

HEY, ALL MY STUFF IS IN THE TRASH CAN!

THAT'S A FUNNY THING TO CALL YOUR PERSONAL STORAGE UNIT.

I AM MORDAC, THE PREVENTER OF INFORMATION SERVICES. I BRING NEW GUIDELINES FOR PASSWORDS.

"ALL PASSWORDS MUST BE AT LEAST SIX CHARACTERS LONG... INCLUDE NUMBERS AND LETTERS... INCLUDE A MIX OF UPPER AND LOWER CASE..."

"USE DIFFERENT PASS-WORDS FOR EACH SYSTEM. CHANGE ONCE A MONTH. DO NOT WRITE ANY-THING DOWN."

SQUEAL LIKE A PIG!!!

I AM MORDAC, THE PREVENTER OF INFORMATION SERVICES. I COME TO CONFISCATE YOUR NON-STANDARD COMPUTER.

YOU'LL GIVE ME A NEW ONE, RIGHT?

THIS IS HEAVIER THAN IT LOOKS.

I'LL HAVE TO DISABLE IT AND LEAVE IT HERE.

THE NEW ONE IS ALREADY ON ITS WAY, RIGHT?

I'M GLAD HE QUIT. HE WAS SUCH AN OBNOXIOUS, USELESS CO-WORKER.

WE HAD TO BE NICE TO HIM BECAUSE WE NEEDED HIS COOPERATION.

THE JERK!

HE SHOULD CHECK THE EXPIRATION DATE ON HIS COLOGNE!

NEXT TIME, I WILL NOT GIVE TWO WEEKS' NOTICE.

I'M COLLECTING FOR ED'S FAREWELL GIFT.

ED, YOU TREATED ME LIKE DIRT. I FIND YOU GUILTY AND I FINE YOU FIVE DOLLARS.

I JUST PUT THAT IN THERE.

COME BACK IF YOU GET MORE.

HEH HEH. ED IS BARELY OUT THE DOOR AND I GOT HIS OLD COMPUTER.

THE SCAVENGING WAS GOOD TODAY.

ALICE IS GOING TO BE MIFFED THAT SHE'S TOO LATE FOR THE GOOD STUFF.

YOU GOT HIS PANTS?

IT WASN'T EASY. HE'D ALREADY MADE IT TO THE BUS.

I CRITICIZE MY CO-WORKERS TO MAKE MYSELF LOOK SMART.

S. Adams

APPARENTLY IT ISN'T WORKING.

WHAT DO YOU MEAN BY THAT?

NOTHING.

OOH, THAT REMINDS ME TO ADD NUTS TO MY GROCERY LIST.

I RECOMMEND THAT WE HAVE WEEKLY SESSIONS UNTIL YOU RUN OUT OF MONEY.

4/12/98 © 1998 United Feature Syndicate, Inc.

CAN YOU CURE ME?

NO, I'M PAID BY THE HOUR. I'LL GIVE YOU PROBLEMS YOU'VE NEVER EVEN HEARD OF.

WE HAVE A FEW MINUTES TODAY. WOULD YOU LIKE A FALSE MEMORY?

MAYBE SOMETHING WITH ALIENS?

CATBERT: EVIL H.R. DIRECTOR

YOU LOOK STRESSED OUT, ALICE.

I COULD FIX THAT BY BECOMING A CHAMPION FOR IMPROVEMENTS IN THE WORKPLACE.

OR I COULD GIVE YOU A LITTLE BOOKLET CALLED "STRESS NO MORE."

HMM... I WONDER WHICH WAY IS BEST.

"STRESS IS YOUR BODY'S WAY OF SAYING..."

"... YOU HAVEN'T WORKED ENOUGH UNPAID OVERTIME."

I'VE NEVER SEEN A WOMAN'S FOREHEAD IGNITE HER HAIR BEFORE.

160

ALICE, I'M THE NEW GUY. I LOOK SMARTER THAN THE PEOPLE WHO ALREADY WORK HERE.

AS YOU GET TO KNOW ME, I'LL LOOK DUMBER AND DUMBER.

THAT WAS FAST.

OOGA.

DILBERT, THIS IS ALLEN, MY NEW SYCOPHANT.

HIS HEAD NODS WHENEVER I TALK. BUT THAT'S NOT THE BEST PART...

VERY IMPRESSIVE.

IS THAT GREAT OR WHAT?

SO, ALLEN, WHAT'S IT LIKE TO BE A HIDEOUS SYCOPHANT?

IT'S OKAY.

WHAT'S IT LIKE TO HAVE NO HOPE OF CAREER ADVANCEMENT?

NOT BAD.

WERE YOU BORN THAT WAY OR IS IT A LIFESTYLE CHOICE?

I'LL ASK MOM, BUT I THINK IT WAS BAD PARENTING.

ARE YOU THE POMPOUS AIRBAG OF THE OFFICE?

INDEED.

I'VE BEEN ASKED TO DEFLATE YOU.

MY SOURCES TELL ME THAT YOU COMBINE ARROGANCE WITH TRIVIA AND TRY TO PASS IT OFF AS INTELLIGENCE.

THAT'S BECAUSE I'M SURROUNDED BY FOOLS WHO DON'T EVEN KNOW THE CAPITAL OF ELBONIA!

I HAVE A SIGNED STATEMENT FROM YOUR WIFE...

...THAT YOU PUT WET LAUNDRY IN THE OVEN LAST NIGHT.

THAT EXPLAINS THE CHEWY CASSEROLE SHE SERVED ME THIS MORNING.

DOGBERT THE C.E.O.

I'VE DECIDED TO MANIPULATE OUR STOCK PRICE FOR PERSONAL GAIN.

I'LL SPIN OFF A FEW DIVISIONS, BUY BACK SOME OF OUR STOCK AND ANNOUNCE MASSIVE BUDGET CUTS.

UM... DO YOU EVEN KNOW WHAT PRODUCTS WE MAKE?

HOW WOULD THAT BE RELEVANT?

I HIRED MY SON TO MANAGE OUR TECH-NOLOGY DEVELOPMENT GROUP.

HE'S YOUNG, BUT I'M ALMOST POSITIVE HE WENT TO COLLEGE.

WHERE DID YOU GO TO COLLEGE?

ACTUALLY, I HID IN OUR ATTIC FOR FOUR YEARS.

MY DAD TAUGHT ME EVERYTHING I KNOW.

HE USED TO SAY "DON'T DRINK THE PICKLE JUICE UNTIL THE PICKLES ARE GONE."

WAS THAT A BIG PROBLEM AT YOUR HOUSE?

HAVE YOU EVER BEEN HIT IN THE EYE WITH A PICKLE?

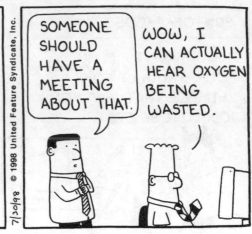

IT'S NOT MY POLICY TO FIRE MORONS, DONALD. FIRING IS EXPENSIVE.

IT'S MY POLICY TO MAKE YOUR JOB SO UNPLEASANT THAT YOU QUIT.

SO, YOUR PROJECT INVOLVES BEING BITTEN BY COYOTES?

ONLY TWO MORE YEARS AND I'M VESTED.

ACCORDING TO HIS DRIVER'S LICENSE, THE NEW GUY'S NAME IS EDWARD MANN.

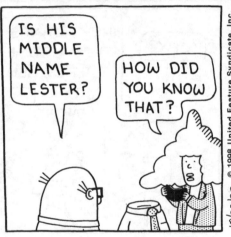

IS HIS MIDDLE NAME LESTER?

HOW DID YOU KNOW THAT?

WHAT WE HAVE HERE IS AN ED LES MANN.

THANK YOU ALL FOR COMING TO THE MEETING THAT HAS NO REAL PURPOSE.

MAYBE WE COULD RAISE ISSUES AND THEN FORM ACTION PLANS.

I HAVE AN URGE TO STOMP YOU TO DEATH.

THAT'S NOT VERY PROFESSIONAL OF YOU.

CATBERT THE DIRECTOR OF HUMAN RESOURCES

SO, YOU WANT A JOB HERE, TUBBY?

IT'S "TOBY."

DID YOU JUST CORRECT ME?

UM...

I ALONE WILL DETERMINE YOUR NAME!!

NOW, WHAT IS YOUR NAME?

TUBBY.

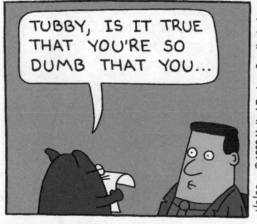

TUBBY, IS IT TRUE THAT YOU'RE SO DUMB THAT YOU...

...SENT YOUR RÉSUMÉ TO THE HUMAN RESOURCES DEPARTMENT?

DO YOU THINK THAT'S WHAT THIS DEPARTMENT DOES? LET ME SHOW YOU WHAT I DO.

I THINK I JUST BECAME AN ENTREPRENEUR.

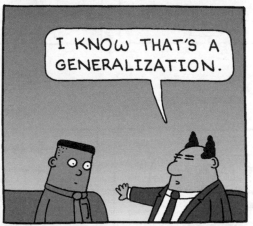

WHY DO YOU SEEK MORDAC — THE PREVENTER OF INFORMATION SERVICES?

I REGRET SENDING AN INSULTING E-MAIL MESSAGE TO OUR CIO. I NEED TO DELETE IT FROM THE SERVER.

THE SERVER WAS IN THAT CLOSET, RIGHT?

THAT'S THE CIO'S OFFICE.

YOU'VE ALL BEEN CHOSEN FOR THIS TEAM BECAUSE OF YOUR TALENT AND PROFESSIONALISM.

EXCEPT FOR DAN, WHO IS A BIG STUBBORN GUY WHO WILL PREVENT OUR SUCCESS.

SHALL WE COMMENCE FAILING?

I CAN'T DO WORK WITHOUT A VISION STATEMENT.

BIG STUBBORN DUMB GUY

WE SHOULD REMOVE THE CONTRACT EMPLOYEES FROM OUR E-MAIL BULLETIN LIST.

UM... THEY NEED THAT INFORMATION TO DO THEIR JOBS, AND THERE'S NO INCREMENTAL COST.

THIS IS WHEN YOU AGREE WITH ME AND WE MOVE ON WITH OUR LIVES.

I WILL FIGHT YOU TO THE END OF THE EARTH!

THERE'S NO REASON TO BE STRESSED, ALICE.

ALLOW ME TO BE YOUR ROLE MODEL.

I REMAIN CALM DESPITE THE PRESSURE OF IMPOSSIBLE DEADLINES.

THAT'S BECAUSE YOU HAVE NO PRIDE AND NO AMBITION!

I'VE WORKED DAY AND NIGHT TO MAKE THIS DEAD-LINE!

AND WHEN I SUCCEED, THE GLORY WILL BE MINE!

OUR NEW VP JUST CANCELED THE PROJECT SO THE LAST VP WOULD LOOK BAD.

THEY SAY THAT WHEN THE STUDENT IS READY, THE MASTER WILL APPEAR.

I'M RELOCATING TO A BETTER CUBICLE.

TONIGHT A TEAM OF MOVERS WILL TAKE MY BOXED POSSESSIONS TO AN UNDISCLOSED LOCATION.

THEY'RE ALSO GOING TO LAMINATE MY COMPANY I.D.

I'M SUPPOSED TO LEAVE IT WITH THE GUARD ON THE WAY OUT.

AND I GOT PAID TWO DAYS EARLY!

IT'S ALL BECAUSE MANAGEMENT APPRECIATED THE CONSTRUCTIVE CRITICISM I POSTED ON THE MESSAGE BOARD.

AS I HOPED, MY CONDESCENDING TONE HELPED THEM TO SEE THEIR FOLLY.

DO YOU MIND IF I RIFLE THROUGH YOUR BOXES AND TAKE OFFICE SUPPLIES?

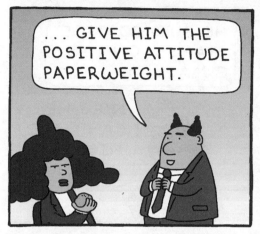

184

185

187

ED, THE EXPERTS SAY MANAGERS SHOULD OVER-COMMUNICATE DURING TIMES OF UNCERTAINTY.

YOU'RE FIRED, YOU'RE FIRED, YOU'RE FIRED, YOU'RE FIRED, YOU'RE FIRED!

I'LL COME BACK IN TEN MINUTES TO DO THAT AGAIN.

I'M STRESSED OUT ABOUT WORK. MAYBE I'D FEEL BETTER IF I VERBALLY ABUSED A CO-WORKER.

YOU WORTHLESS PIECE OF MONKEY SPIT!

DANG. I WAS GOING TO USE THAT ONE.

AAH....

LET ME DO ALL THE TALKING TO THE CUSTOMER.

CHECK!

YOU'D BETTER MAKE UP YOUR MIND FAST. WE PLAN TO DISCONTINUE THAT PRODUCT ANY DAY.

WELL, EXCUSE ME FOR TRYING TO FILL A LULL IN THE CONVERSATION.

THE TECHNOLOGY DEMO

THE SOFTWARE ISN'T 100% COMPLETE.

IF IT HAD A USER INTERFACE YOU WOULD SEE SOMETHING HERE... HERE...AND SOMETIMES HERE.

AND THEN YOU'D BE SAYING, "I GOTTA GET ME SOME OF THAT."

ANY QUESTIONS?

TED RESIGNED. YOUR JOB IS TO FIND OUT WHERE HE HID HIS FILES.

OUR ONLY CLUE IS THAT HE WAS DISGRUNTLED.

NEGATORY ON PORCELAIN PATTY.

I HAVE FOUND WHERE TED HID HIS FILES BEFORE HE QUIT.

A SKELETON!

I KNOW WHAT I MUST DO.

WHO'S THE BABE?

STAY AWAY, HOMEWRECKER.

CAN YOU SING OR DANCE?

TED? I THOUGHT YOU RESIGNED IN DISGUST TWO WEEKS AGO.

WELL... I WROTE A HUGE RESIGNATION MANIFESTO THAT I PLANNED TO E-MAIL TO THE ENTIRE COMPANY.

BUT I THOUGHT IT NEEDED PICTURES.

BEFORE LONG I WAS ADDING VIDEO CLIPS AND HUMOROUS SOUND FILES.

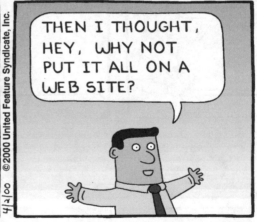

THEN I THOUGHT, HEY, WHY NOT PUT IT ALL ON A WEB SITE?

NOW I'M TURNING THE WHOLE THING INTO AN OFF BROADWAY THEATRE PRODUCTION.

I SAW MY FIRST MOTIVATED EMPLOYEE TODAY.

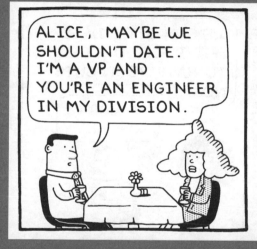

I FINISHED UPGRADING THE SALES SUPPORT NETWORK.

IS THAT WHY I CAN'T UNLOCK MY LEXUS?!!

YOU DON'T OWN A LEXUS. YOU ONLY LOOK LIKE A GUY DOWN THE HALL WHO OWNS ONE.

I HATE THAT GUY.

TED, I'M GIVING YOU A PROMOTION IN TITLE.

WOW!

NOW YOU'RE THE SENIOR VICE DUKE AND IMPERIAL MAJESTY OF ALL ENGINEERING.

CAN I HAVE BUSINESS CARDS NOW?

NO, YOU'RE ONLY A VICE DUKE.

TED, YOUR TEN YEAR SERVICE PARTY WILL BE ON TUESDAY.

I'M HAVING SURGERY TUESDAY.

MAYBE YOU COULD DROP OFF A CASSEROLE ON YOUR WAY.

TED, YOUR THIRTY-DAY DANCE OF DEATH BEGINS TODAY.

YOU MUST FIND A NEW JOB WITHIN THE COMPANY DURING THAT TIME.

IS THE SPRAY-PAINT ABSOLUTELY NECESSARY?

THAT'S AN "L."

I NEED A NEW JOB WITHIN THE COMPANY BEFORE THE WINDOW SHUTS.

CATBERT IS ALREADY UP TO "O." NEXT WEEK HE GETS AN "S."

WHAT'S HE SPELLING?

HE WOULDN'T SAY, BUT IT STARTS WITH AN "L."

CATBERT SAYS I HAVE TO GET A NEW JOB WITHIN THE COMPANY.

COULD YOU FIND IT WITHIN YOUR HEART...

I'LL CHECK.

NOPE. NO JOBS IN THERE.

TODAY IS MY LAST DAY. I'M SAYING MY FAREWELLS.

WE'VE NEVER TALKED, BUT I WAS WORKING MY WAY DOWN THE ROW AND HERE YOU ARE.

SO... LET'S STAY IN TOUCH.

DON'T BE A STRANGER.

I'LL SEE IF THE GUYS IN MARKETING KNOW FIRST AID.

REALLY? I PICKED THAT INTERN IN OUR ENGINEERING DEAD POOL!

APPARENTLY OUR TEAM-BUILDING POTLUCK LUNCH DIDN'T TAKE.

I'M ALIVE!

WHICH ONE OF YOU ANGELS ADMINISTERED THE LIFE-SAVING CPR?

SPEAKING OF "LIFESAVERS," I COULD SURE USE ONE RIGHT NOW.

DILBERT, MEET TOPPER. HE'S AMAZING.

NO MATTER WHAT YOU SAY ABOUT YOURSELF, HE'LL TOP IT.

HOW ARE YOU?

I CAN'T GO FIRST. IT RUINS MY SYSTEM.

UM...MORDAC, MY NEW PC ARRIVED WITHOUT A MONITOR.

BAH! ONLY INTERNS WITH WEAK MEMORIES NEED MONITORS!

PLEASE. I AM HAVING ENOUGH DIFFICULTY MEMORIZING MY CALENDAR.

DID YOU WANT ANY CHEESE WITH THAT WHINE?

I HIRED A CREEP TO HELP DETERMINE OUR PRODUCT'S FEATURES.

YOU NEED MORE FEATURES.

GOOD WORK.

WHEN CAN YOU HAVE THAT DONE?

GAAA!!

THE FEATURE CREEP

IS IT TOO LATE TO GIVE OUR PRODUCT A LOW-BATTERY INDICATOR?

I'D HAVE TO WORK NIGHT AND DAY FOR A MONTH! MY HEALTH WOULD DECLINE AND I'D MISS ALL MY OBJECTIVES!

I JUST REALIZED THAT OTHER PEOPLE'S PROBLEMS MAKE ME ALL WARM INSIDE.

THE FEATURE CREEP

BEING A FEATURE CREEP IS LIKE HAVING A SUPER POWER.

THAT'S WHAT MAKES ME SO SEXY.

OOMP

THAT OOMP SOUND JUST BOUGHT YOU A NEW FEATURE, MISSY.

MY FLIGHT DIDN'T GET IN UNTIL THREE THIS MORNING.

WOULD YOU MIND SLAPPING THE BACK OF MY HEAD UNTIL MY EYES UNCROSS?

POUR ALL OF YOUR COFFEE IN HERE AND NO ONE GETS HURT.

MY NEPHEW WANTS A JOB. INTERVIEW HIM AND TELL ME WHAT YOU THINK.

LET'S SEE... YOUR WORK EXPERIENCE IS... BOWLING.

ARE YOU A PROFESSIONAL BOWLER?

I ONLY BOWLED ONCE.

BUT THE BALLS WERE HEAVY. IT SEEMED LIKE WORK TO ME.

THAT EXPERIENCE TAUGHT ME EVERYTHING I KNOW.

UNFORTUNATELY, I DON'T REMEMBER MOST OF IT.

BUT I REMEMBER YOU'RE NOT SUPPOSED TO BOWL IN THE SNACK BAR.

I RECOMMEND HAVING HIM WHACKED.

HE'S YOUR NEW BOSS.

MY FLIGHT TOOK ALL NIGHT BUT I STILL CAME TO WORK ON TIME AS USUAL.

I DIDN'T WANT TO JEOPARDIZE THE COMPANY BY MISSING WORK.

YOU'RE NOT ALLOWED TO PARK IN THE LOBBY.

SINCE WHEN?!

SMILE, ALICE. IT WON'T HURT.

GAAAK!!

I FOUND OUT I CAN KILL PEOPLE BY LOOKING AT THEM.

I WONDERED WHY YOU WERE SMILING.

WHAT IS THIS STRANGE AND BEAUTIFUL FEELING INSIDE OF ME?!

WAVES OF ECSTASY ARE PULSING THROUGH MY SOUL.

THIS IS WHY I ONLY GIVE POSITIVE REINFORCEMENT ONCE A YEAR.

I'M ALL TINGLY!

I EXPERIENCED SOMETHING CALLED POSITIVE REINFORCEMENT TODAY.

I'M ADDICTED TO IT NOW... BUT IT'S WEARING OFF... MUST GET MORE...

SAY SOMETHING NICE ABOUT ME!

FOR A CRAZY WOMAN YOU DON'T DROOL MUCH.

I'M ADDICTED TO POSITIVE REINFORCEMENT.

I NEED SOME DELIVERABLES SO I CAN BE PRAISED AGAIN.

RESULTS

10%

I'M A BIT SUSPICIOUS ABOUT YOU CALLING IN SICK YESTERDAY ON A MONDAY, ALICE.

GLAH!

LUCKILY I HAD LOTS OF OPTIONAL GUTS.

TINA, I HAVE TO GIVE YOU A PERFORMANCE RATING OF "POOR" BECAUSE YOU DID NO WORK THIS YEAR.

NO WORK?

I WROTE HUNDREDS OF TECHNICAL DOCUMENTS THIS YEAR!

I WORKED SEVENTY HOURS A WEEK!

I E-MAILED EVERY ONE OF THE DOCUMENTS TO YOU...

...WITH INSTRUCTIONS TO FORWARD THEM WITH YOUR APPROVAL TO THE END USERS.

THAT REMINDS ME: I DON'T KNOW HOW TO OPEN ATTACHMENTS.

WHY DIDN'T YOU TELL ME YOU NEVER GOT MY DOCUMENTS?

WHO ARE YOU?

I'M SAFE FROM YOUR GERMS, ALICE. YOU CAN SNEEZE ALL YOU WANT.

AAH...

WE NEED TO REDUCE STAFF BY TWENTY.

HERE'S A LIST OF THE PEOPLE YOU'VE A-L-M-O-S-T WORKED TO DEATH.

I HAVE ANOTHER PROJECT FOR YOU ...UH...TED.

AACK!

...AND SO YOU AGREE THAT THE DELAYS ARE YOUR FAULT?

YEH.

I WON THE MEETING!!

ONLY A SORE LOSER WOULD TRIP SOMEONE ON HIS VICTORY LAP.

HE IS SO-O-O IMMATURE.

CATBERT: EVIL H.R. DIRECTOR

...AND I HAVE FIVE YEARS EXPERIENCE AS A DOT-COM PRESIDENT.

YOU'RE IN LUCK. WE NEED SOMEONE WHO CAN BURN THROUGH TWENTY MILLION DOLLARS WITHOUT MAKING A PROFIT.

REALLY? THE LAST NINE INTERVIEWERS SAID THE SAME THING BUT THEY WERE JOKING.

DUE TO A TIGHT LABOR MARKET AND INCREASINGLY COMPLICATED TASKS...

AAIEE!

HARDER AND HARDER JOBS WILL BE STAFFED WITH DUMBER AND DUMBER EMPLOYEES UNTIL THE LOGICAL LIMIT:

THIS MEETING.

YOUR USER REQUIRE-MENTS INCLUDE FOUR HUNDRED FEATURES.

DO YOU REALIZE THAT NO HUMAN WOULD BE ABLE TO USE A PRODUCT WITH THAT LEVEL OF COMPLEXITY?

GOOD POINT. I'D BETTER ADD "EASY TO USE" TO THE LIST.

THE TOO HELPFUL GUY

DILBERT, MEET THE NEW GUY.

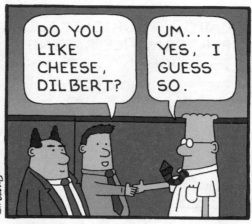

DO YOU LIKE CHEESE, DILBERT?

UM... YES, I GUESS SO.

I'LL SEND TWO TRUCKLOADS OF PARMESAN CHEESE TO YOUR HOUSE!

THANKS... BUT I DON'T NEED THAT MUCH CHEESE.

MESSAGE RECEIVED!

I'LL SEND YOU SOME BREAD AND A FONDUE SET TOO.

HERE ARE TWO TICKETS TO THE "WORLD-O-CHEESE" EXHIBIT IN WISCONSIN.

YOUR NEW NICKNAME WILL BE "CHEESEBOY" TO REFLECT YOUR WEIRD OBSESSION.

HI. I'M WALLY.

WALLY, DO YOU LIKE LEATHER PRODUCTS?

CAROL, YOUR OVERALL PERFORMANCE RATING IS "GOOD."

AAAG! GOOD IS BAD! WHAT DID I DO TO DESERVE THIS HUMILIATION.

WELL, YOU GAVE ME SIX HUNDRED PHONE MESSAGES THAT SAID, "IT MIGHT HAVE BEEN BOB."

YOU CAN'T TELL ME THAT NONE OF THEM WERE FROM A BOB!

YOU ARRANGED FOR ALL OF MY FLIGHTS TO HAVE CONNECTIONS IN WAR ZONES.

EXCUSE ME FOR TRYING TO SAVE THE COMPANY SOME MONEY.

YOU HELD A PRESS CONFERENCE TO ANNOUNCE THAT I WAS THE PARKSIDE STRANGLER.

AND HE REFUSES TO TAKE ANY RESPONSIBILITY FOR GIVING ME VAGUE OBJECTIVES.

THIS IS JITTERY JEFF. HE NEEDS COUNSELING.

I PUT HIM IN A CUBICLE AT THE END OF A BUSY AISLE NEAR A DOORWAY.

NOW HE'S JITTERY BECAUSE HE THINKS PEOPLE ARE ALWAYS LOOKING OVER HIS SHOULDER.

LEAVE HIM HERE. I'LL COUNSEL HIM UP.

RELAX, JITTERY JEFF... IT'S OKAY NOW.

RELAX
RELAX
RELAX
RELAX

5|20|01 © 2001 United Feature Syndicate, Inc.

AAAGH!! SOMEONE IS BEHIND THE DOOR!!

COUNSELING IS MOSTLY INSTINCT.

I DOWNSIZED TED AND OUTSOURCED HIS IMPORTANT JOB FUNCTIONS.

I'D LIKE YOU TO DO ALL OF HIS UNIMPORTANT JOB FUNCTIONS.

WHY DO WE DO UNIMPORTANT THINGS?

BECAUSE WE CAN!

DILBERT, I'D LIKE YOU TO MEET INCREDULOUS ED.

NO MATTER WHAT QUESTION YOU ASK HIM, HE'LL REACT AS IF YOU'RE INVENTING WORDS.

DO YOU HAVE A FAMILY?

DO I HAVE A **WHAT**??

INCREDULOUS ED

ED, DO YOU HAVE THE LATEST BUDGET NUMBERS?

BUDGET??? WHAT IS A "BUDGET"? AND WHY IN THE WORLD WOULD I HAVE ONE?

BECAUSE YOU'RE THE BUDGET MANAGER.

HERE YOU GO.

I CAN'T GIVE YOU A RAISE BECAUSE YOU DON'T ASK ENOUGH QUESTIONS IN MEETINGS.

QUESTIONS SHOW THAT YOU CARE ABOUT YOUR JOB AND HAVE A THIRST FOR KNOWLEDGE.

WHO ELSE LIKES WOOD?

WE SHOULD READ THE SET-UP INSTRUCTIONS.

ALICE, A TRUE ENGINEER NEVER READS THE SET-UP INSTRUCTIONS.

IT SAYS TO KEEP IT AWAY FROM ANY SLURPING SOUNDS.

GAAA!!

FRANKLY, THE JOB IS A REAL NO-BRAINER.

YOUR RÉSUMÉ IS A BLANK PIECE OF PAPER; I LIKE A MAN WHO CAN BE BRIEF.

YOU'RE RUINING MY DONUT EXPERIENCE.

I'M SORRY, BRIAN. I NEED TO FIRE ALL OF MY CONSULTANTS TO SAVE MONEY.

WHO WILL DO YOUR HIGHLY TECHNICAL WORK?

YOU CAN TRANSFER YOUR KNOWLEDGE TO FLOSSIE.

HI.

WHAT'S WITH THE HAND? DO YOU WANT TO BORROW MY PENCIL?

UM...NO. THIS IS AN INVITATION TO SHAKE HANDS. IT'S A GREETING RITUAL.

© 2001 United Feature Syndicate, Inc.

6/3/01

OUCH!! BRAIN OVERLOAD!! IT'S TOO MUCH INFORMATION!!

PURGE! PURGE! PURGE!

WHERE AM I?

I NEED TO RAISE MY RATES.

THE ANGRY DUMB GUY

IF ANYONE WANTS MY OPINION...

...I'LL BEAT IT OUT OF ME!

I WANT YOUR OPINION.

OH YEAH? LET'S SEE IF I HAVE ONE!

THE EXIT INTERVIEW

WHAT WOULD YOU SAY IS YOUR MAIN REASON FOR LEAVING?

I CAN'T STAND WORKING FOR AN UNETHICAL WEASEL.

YEP, PERSONAL PROBLEMS.

I'M GLAD THAT WE COLLECT THIS HELPFUL DATA.

CAROL, ORDER A NEW CHAIR FOR ME. THE OLD ONE LOST ITS NEW CHAIR SMELL.

CAN I HAVE YOUR OLD CHAIR? MY CHAIR DOESN'T ROLL ANYMORE.

I'LL TRY TO SAY THIS TACTFULLY: YOU'RE NOT IMPORTANT ENOUGH TO SIT IN MY SMELLY CHAIR.

ALICE, MEET OUR NEW SALES MANAGER.

HE'S A PIGBOY WHO MAKES INAPPROPRIATE COMMENTS EVERY FIVE MINUTES.

S. Adams

SOMEHOW HE SLIPPED THROUGH OUR RIGOROUS EMPLOYMENT SCREENING PROCESS.

WHOA! HIS FIVE MINUTES ARE UP.

SO, ALICE...

INAPPROPRIATE COMMENT DELETED

THAT WAS VERY CLEVER. NOW LET ME TRY ONE.

© 2001 United Feature Syndicate, Inc.
9/2/01

INAPPROPRIATE COMMENT DELETED

HOW DID YOU LEARN TO SWEAR LIKE THAT?

I USED TO DATE A ONE-EYED CARPENTER.